Contents

I Like Cars 3

Fishing with Grandad 13

Prue Looks Like Sue 23

Brian, My Friend 33

My Skeleton 43

Learnalot 53

Zolar and the Children 63

What Shall We Call the Kitten? 73

The Bungee Jump 83

Little Duck's Walk 93

Yummy in My Tummy 103

Turtle Eggs 113

It's for You 123

The Worst Haircut in the World 133

Ooh! Aah! 143

The Rollercoaster Ride 153

Fishing with Grandad

Read *Fishing with Grandad.*
Write the words in the spaces. Use the Word Bank.

I went _____ with my Grandad.

We put _____ on our hooks.

We _____ our _____ into the _____ .

Word Bank threw water bait fishing lines

Label the picture. Write the words.
Use the Word Bank.

Word Bank shoe Grandad line hook

4

Stick the pictures.
Match the pictures and sentences.
Write the letters in the circles.

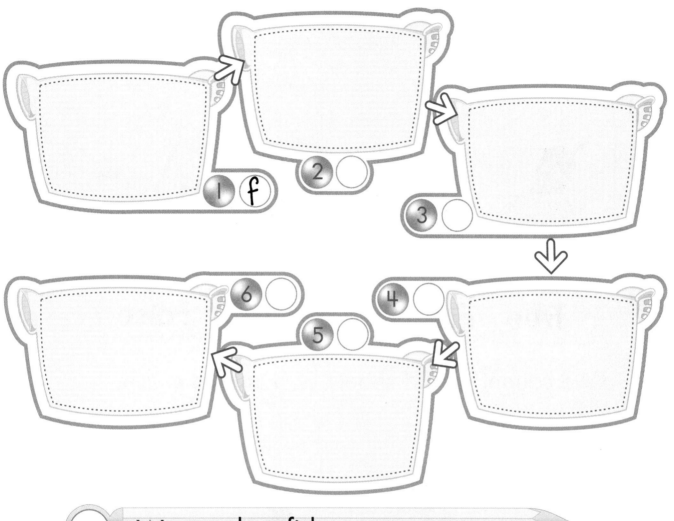

1	f
2	
3	
4	
5	
6	

a We caught a fish.

b We caught some seaweed.

c We threw our lines into the water.

d We caught an old shoe.

e We ate it for dinner.

f We put bait on our hooks.

5

Read the sentences. Circle True or False.

True   False

We caught an old shoe.

True   False

I caught a fish.

True   False

Tug, tug, tug went the line.

True   False

We threw it back.

Stick the stickers to match the pictures.
Write the sentences. Use the Word Bank.

I caught

a _____ .

I caught

some _____ .

Grandad caught

a _____ .

Word Bank   seaweed   shoe   fish

7

Sticker Sheet 2

Stick the stickers to make the sentences.

We [ ] our lines into the water.

We [ ] some seaweed.

Tug, [ ] , tug went the line.

We [ ] it for dinner.

8

Match the number with the word.

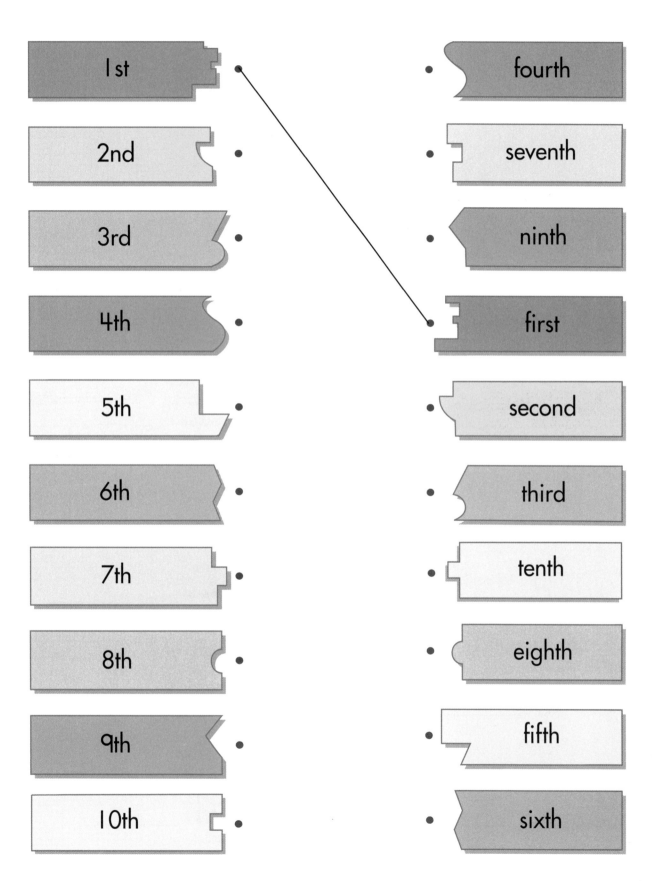

1st	fourth
2nd	seventh
3rd	ninth
4th	first
5th	second
6th	third
7th	tenth
8th	eighth
9th	fifth
10th	sixth

9

Stick the stickers to label the things in the picture.
Write the words. Say the words.

① d_____ ④ w _____

② b _____ ⑤ Gr_____

③ tr_____ ⑥ wh_____

10

© 2006 Wendy Pye Publishing Ltd

Play the game.

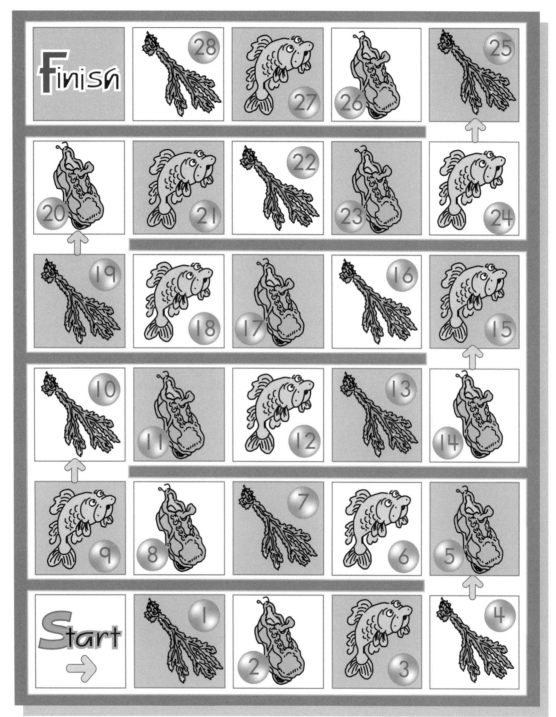

You need: stickers, number cube
1. Stick the stickers to make counters. Put your counters on **Start**.
2. Decide who goes first. Say, "Tug, tug, tug, what have you got?" Then throw the number cube and move your counter the same number of squares.
3. If your counter lands on seaweed or a shoe, say, "Is it a fish? No, it's not!"
   If your counter lands on a fish, say, "Yes, it's a fish for my cooking pot!"
4. The winner is the first player to reach **Finish**.

11

Sticker Sheet 2

Write more words. Use the letters in the Letter Bank. Say the words. Finish the sentences.

Letter Bank   b   b   h   h   m   m   m   n   f

we

___e

___e

___e

tug

___ug

___ug

___ug

line

___ine

___ine

___ine

T___ , ____ , ___ went the _____ .

What had ____ caught this time?

I Like Cars

13

 Read *I Like Cars.* Count the cars.
Write the words. Use the Word Bank.

_____ **car**

_____ **cars**

_____ **cars**

_____ **cars**

Word Bank   one   two   three   four

14

Stick the stickers. Say the sentences.

My cars zoom across the floor.

See me driving in the sun.

I have a new car. It is green.

15

Sticker Sheet 1

Play the game.

You need: stickers, number cube
1. Stick your stickers together to make counters and choose your color—green, red, blue, or yellow.
2. Put your car on **Start**. Decide who goes first. Throw the number cube. Move your car the same number of squares.
3. If your car stops on a square that is called the same color as your car, have another turn.
4. The first player to reach **Finish** is the winner.

16

Stick the stickers to match the color words.
Circle the words in the puzzle.

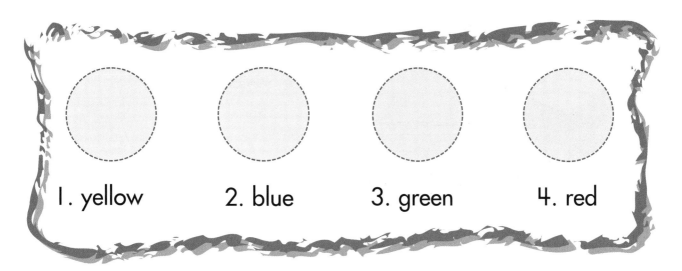

1. yellow   2. blue   3. green   4. red

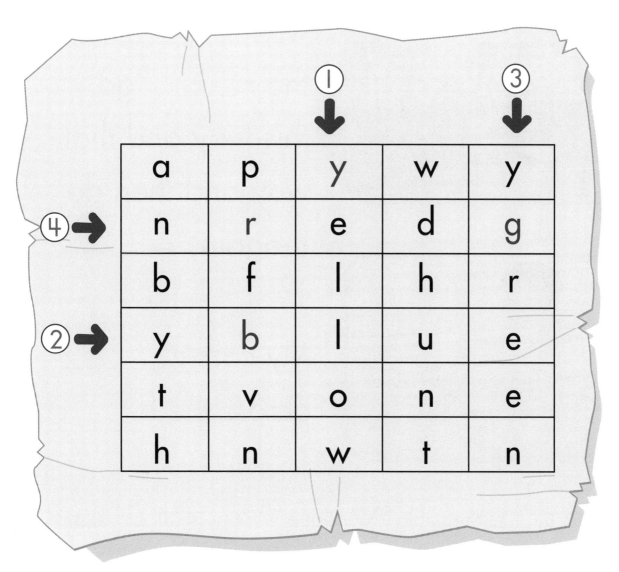

a	p	y	w	y
n	r	e	d	g
b	f	l	h	r
y	b	l	u	e
t	v	o	n	e
h	n	w	t	n

17

Sticker Sheet 1

 Write the words to finish the sentences.
Use the Word Bank.

It's the f_____ car you've ever seen.

W_____ w_____ in the r_____ go this way and that way and then do it again.

My cars z_____ across the f_____ .

Word Bank   zoom rain Windshield wipers floor fastest

 Look at the pictures. Read the words.
Circle **True** or **False**.

I have a new car.

True

False

See me driving in the sun.

True

False

My cars zoom across
the floor.

True

False

Windshield wipers go in
the rain.

True

False

19

Stick the stickers to label the picture.
Write the words to make a sentence.
Use the Word Bank.

I like _____ . Cars are _____ .

See me _____ in the _____ .

Word Bank   driving   sun   cars   fun

These words all begin with **sp-**.
Write the words. Say the words.

sp

_____oon

_____ider

_____y

_____inach

_____aceship

_____aghetti

21

Go through the maze. Follow the letters.
Write each word. Stick the sticker that matches.

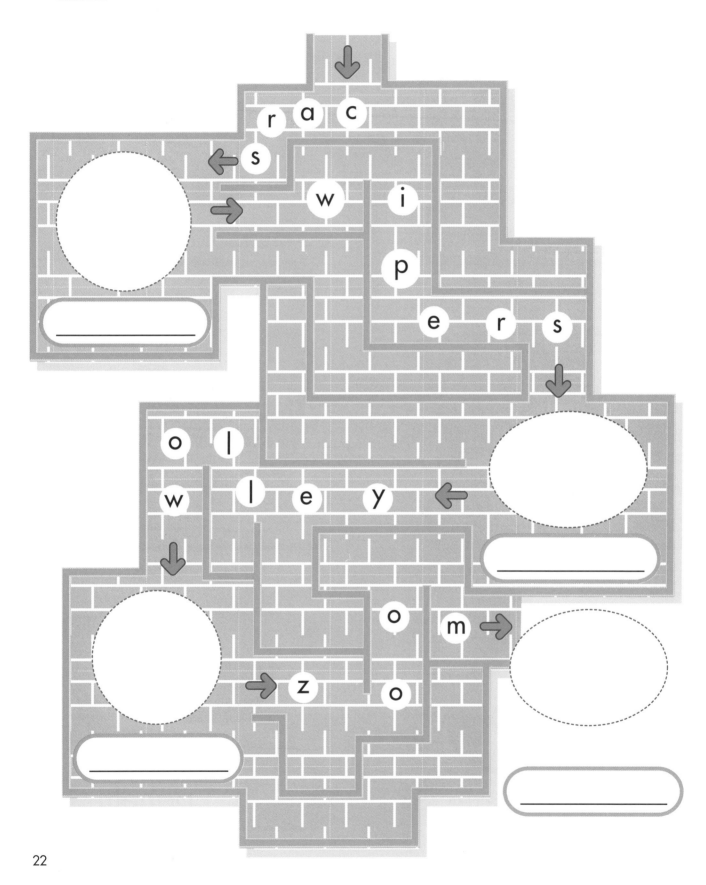

© 2006 Wendy Pye Publishing Ltd

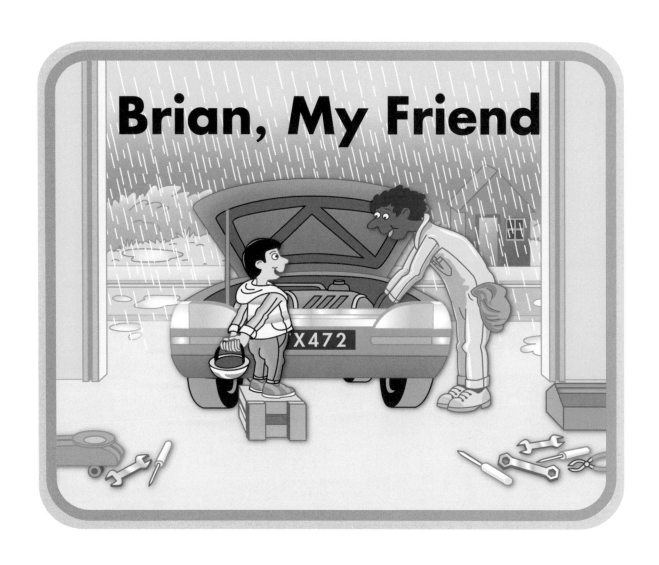

Brian, My Friend

Read *Brian, My Friend*. Go through the maze.
Follow the letters. Write each word.
Stick the stickers that match. Say the words.

Start

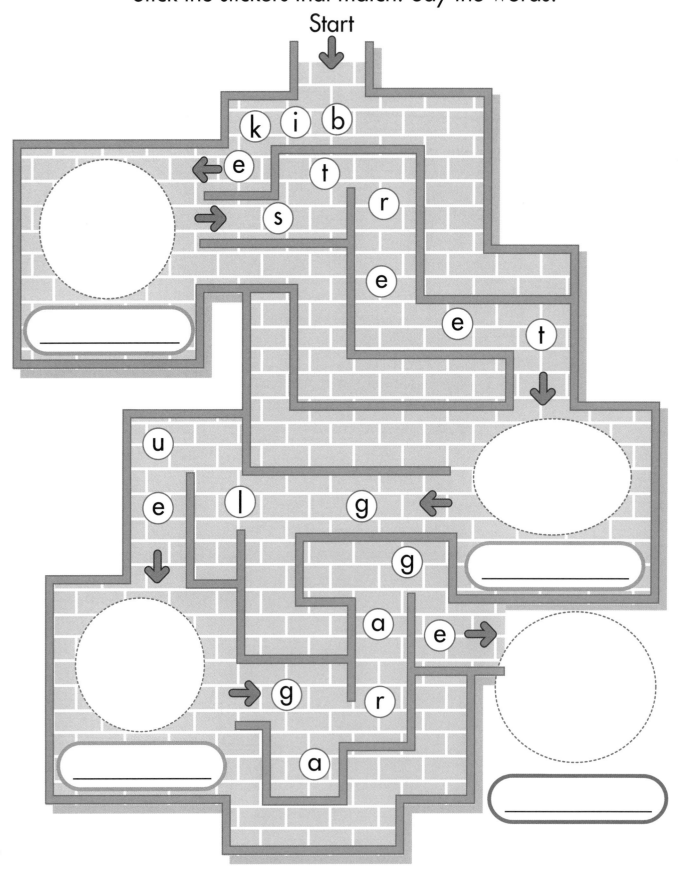

Sticker Sheet 4

© 2006 Wendy Pye Publishing Ltd

Stick the stickers. Look at the pictures.
Write the words. Say the sentences.

A big boy _____ on my bike and _____ the seat.

1

I _____ .

2

4

I _____ Brian a "thank you" letter.

3

Brian _____ my bike.

Sticker Sheet 3

Stick the stickers that begin with **th-**.
Write the words. Say the words.

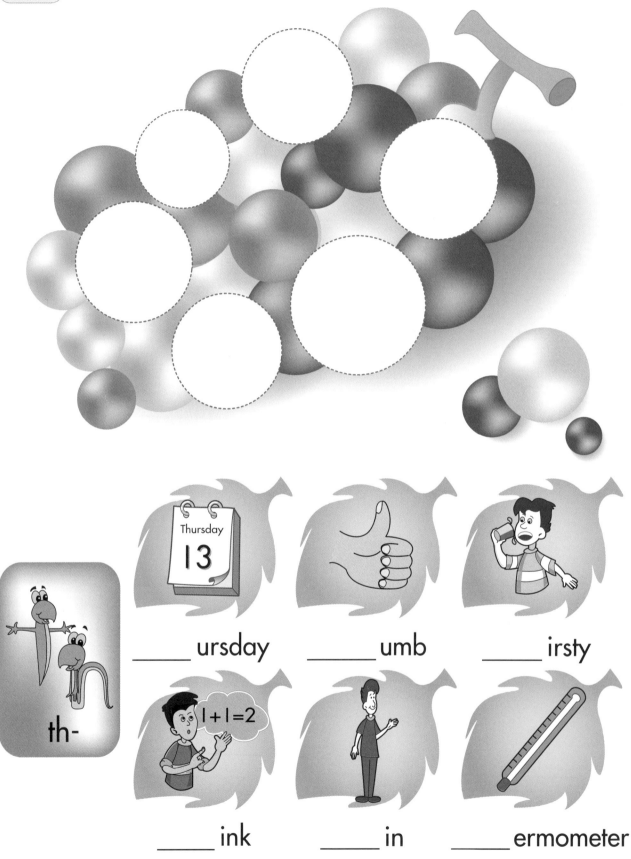

th-

_____ ursday

_____ umb

_____ irsty

_____ ink

_____ in

_____ ermometer

**Read the numbers and words.
Stick the stickers to match.**

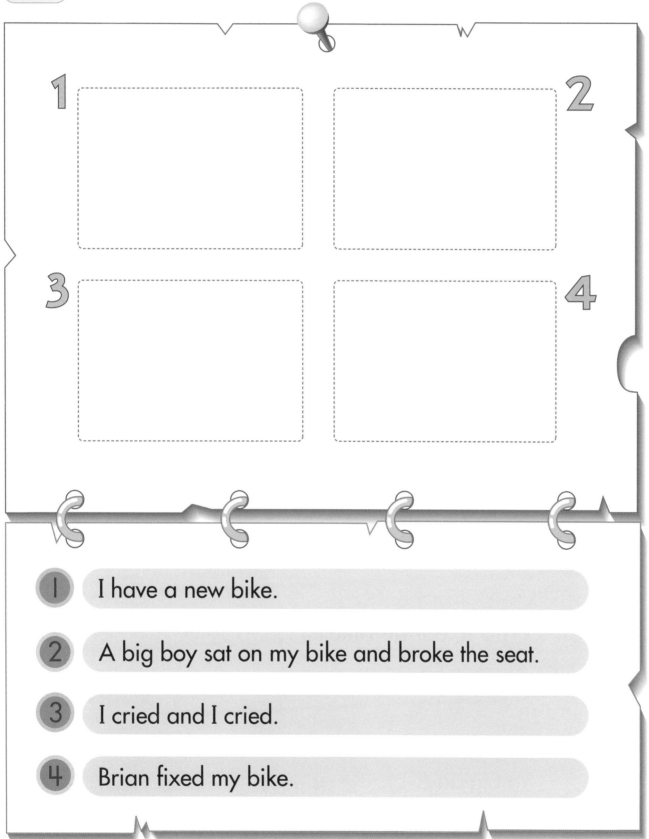

1

2

3

4

1   I have a new bike.

2   A big boy sat on my bike and broke the seat.

3   I cried and I cried.

4   Brian fixed my bike.

Sticker Sheet 3

 Read the questions.
Check the correct answer.

 What color is the bike?

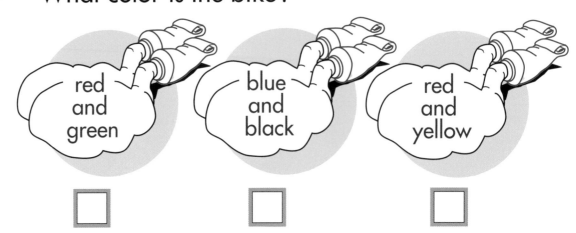

red and green   ☐

blue and black   ☐

red and yellow   ☐

 Who broke the bike?

a big boy   ☐

Brian   ☐

Mom   ☐

 Who fixed the bike?

a big boy   ☐

Brian   ☐

Mom   ☐

28

Play the game.

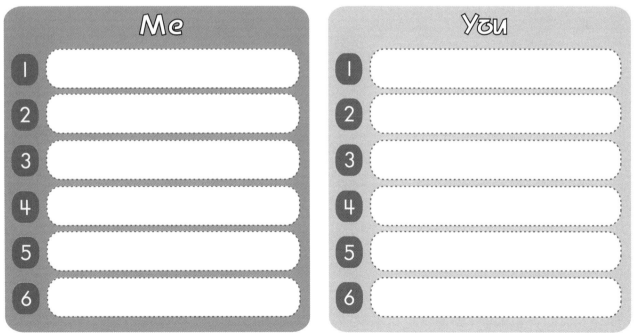

You need: number cube
1. Decide who goes first. Throw the number cube.
2. Stick on the sentence sticker with the same number as the number cube.
3. Read the sentence.
4. The first player to stick on all the sentences is the winner.

29

Sticker Sheet 4

Look at the pictures. Check the correct words to finish the sentences. Write the words. Read the sentences.

A big boy sat on my bike and broke _____.

☐ the wheel

☐ the seat

☐ the handle

A big boy _____ _____ my _____ and _____ _____ _____.

I cried and cried. "Let's go for _____," said Mom.

☐ a ride

☐ a swim

☐ a walk

I cried and cried. "_____ _____ _____ _____ _____," said Mom.

"I can fix this with _____ _____ _____," said Brian.

☐ a hammer

☐ a pen

☐ lots of glue

"I _____ _____ this with _____ _____ _____," said _____.

Color the words that begin with **th-**.
Write the words in the boxes.
Say the words.

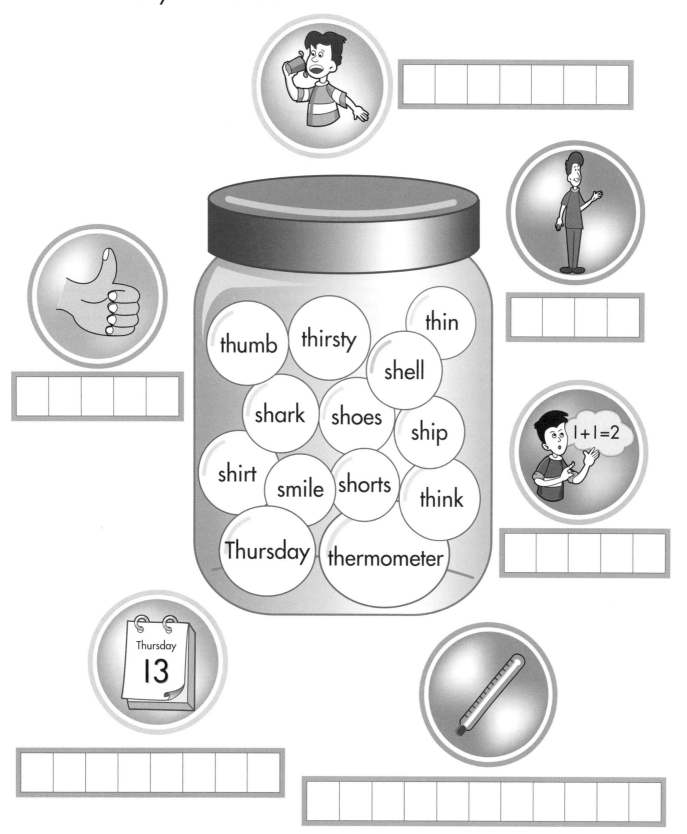

Stick the stickers to label the pictures.
Write the words.
Say the sentences.

_____ _____ _____ who lives up _____ _____

sat on my _____

and _____ _____ _____ .

_____ _____ my _____ and

made me feel better. I _____ Brian

a "thank you" _____ .

Prue Looks Like Sue

Read *Prue Looks Like Sue*. Look at the pictures. Read the words. Circle True or False.

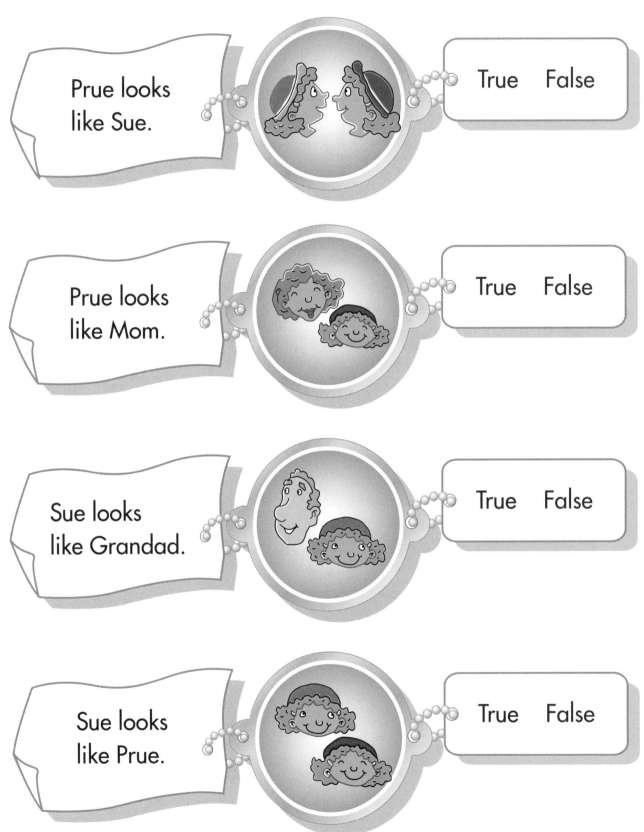

Prue looks like Sue.

True   False

Prue looks like Mom.

True   False

Sue looks like Grandad.

True   False

Sue looks like Prue.

True   False

Look at the pictures. Who do they look like?
Match the pictures.
Write the words. Say the sentences.

Ratty

Patty

Kitty

Bitty

Who looks like Kitty?

_____ looks _____ Kitty.

Pam

Barney

Sam

Arnie

Who looks like Sam?

_____ _____ like Sam.

35

Stick the stickers to finish the puzzle.
Look at the picture clues.
Write the words that begin with **sh-**. Say the words.

sh

_____ip

_____ark

_____ell

_____oes

_____orts

_____irt

36

Write the words. Stick the stickers.
Say the sentences.

I put a red hat on Prue.

I put a blue hat on Sue.

Prue

Sue

I put a green dress on Prue.

I put a yellow dress on Sue.

37

Sticker Sheet 3

Read the questions and answers.
Check the correct answer.

 Grandad can't tell Prue from Sue.
What did Mom do for him?

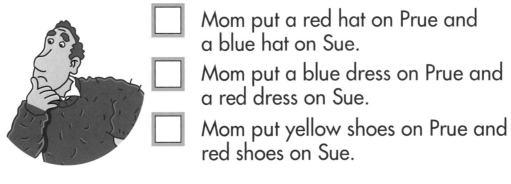

☐ Mom put a red hat on Prue and a blue hat on Sue.

☐ Mom put a blue dress on Prue and a red dress on Sue.

☐ Mom put yellow shoes on Prue and red shoes on Sue.

 Then what did Mom say?

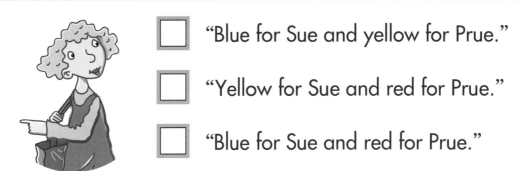

☐ "Blue for Sue and yellow for Prue."

☐ "Yellow for Sue and red for Prue."

☐ "Blue for Sue and red for Prue."

 When Grandad was not looking, what did Prue and Sue do?

☐ Prue put her blue dress on Sue and Sue put her red dress on Prue.

☐ Prue put her red hat on Sue and Sue put her blue hat on Prue.

☐ "Ha, ha, ha!" laughed Sue and Prue.

38

Play the game.

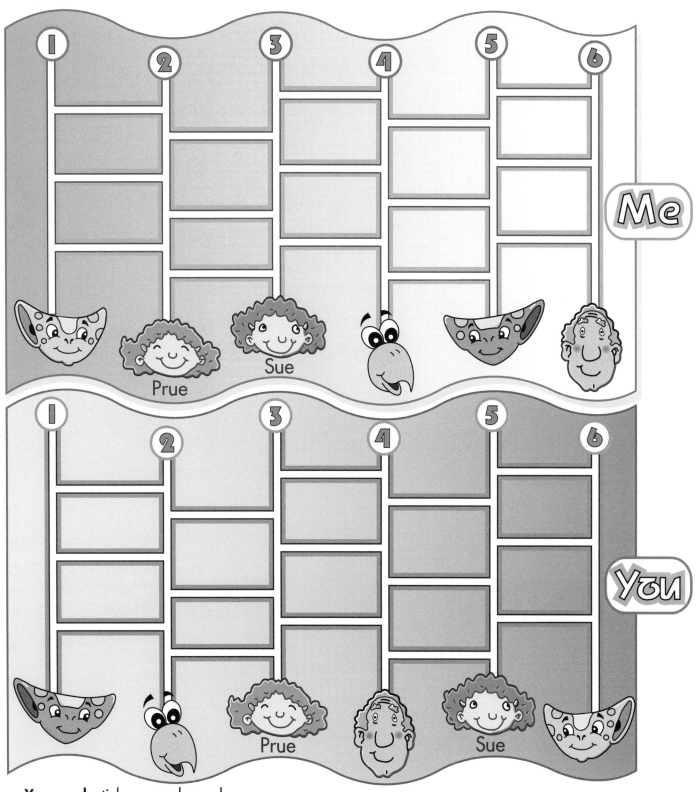

You need: stickers, number cube

1. Decide who goes first. Take six hat stickers each and throw the number cube.
2. Find the person with the same number as the number on the number cube.
   Say, "I put a _____ hat on _____."
3. The first player to put hats on all their characters is the winner.

39

Sticker Sheet 4

 Look at the pictures. Write the words.
Use the Word Bank. Say the sentences.

When Grandad was not looking,

Prue _____ her red hat _____ Sue

and Sue _____ her blue hat

_____ Prue.

"Red _____ Prue," said Grandad,

"and blue _____ Sue.

You are Prue. You are Sue."

"Ha, ha, ha!"

_____ Sue and Prue.

"Ha, ha, ha!"

Mom _____ too.

Word Bank   put   put   on   on   laughed   laughed   for   for

40

Look at the picture clues.
Find the words in the puzzle and circle them.
Write the words in the boxes. Say the words.

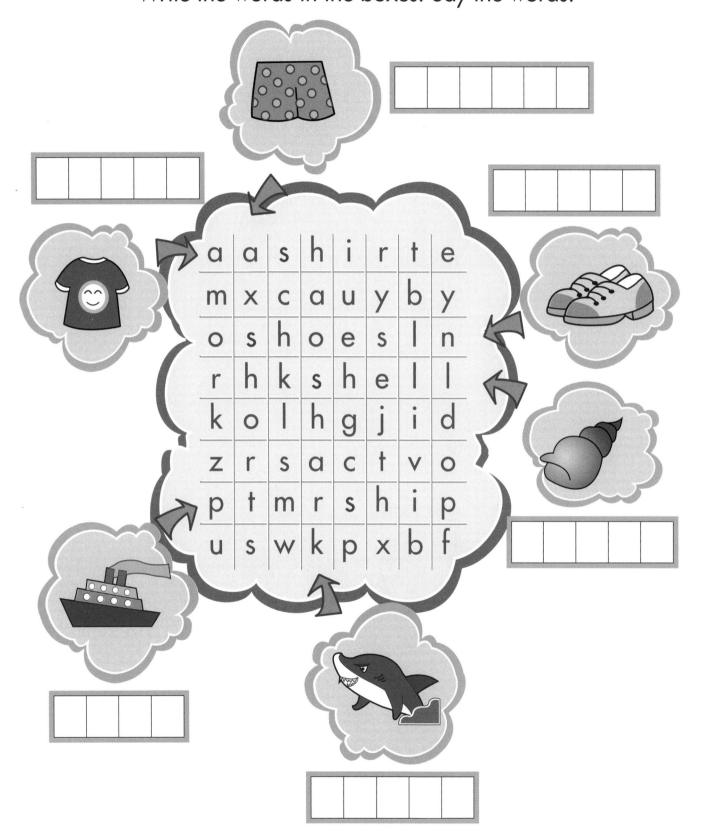

a	a	s	h	i	r	t	e
m	x	c	a	u	y	b	y
o	s	h	o	e	s	l	n
r	h	k	s	h	e	l	l
k	o	l	h	g	j	i	d
z	r	s	a	c	t	v	o
p	t	m	r	s	h	i	p
u	s	w	k	p	x	b	f

41

Look at the pictures.
Make sentences to match.
Write the words. Say the sentences.

Prue looks like Sue
and Sue _____ _____ Prue.
Grandad can't tell Prue from Sue.

Mom put a red hat on Prue
and a blue hat on Sue.
She said, "Blue _____ Sue
and red _____ Prue."

My Skeleton

Read *My Skeleton*. Look at the pictures. Read the words. Circle True or False.

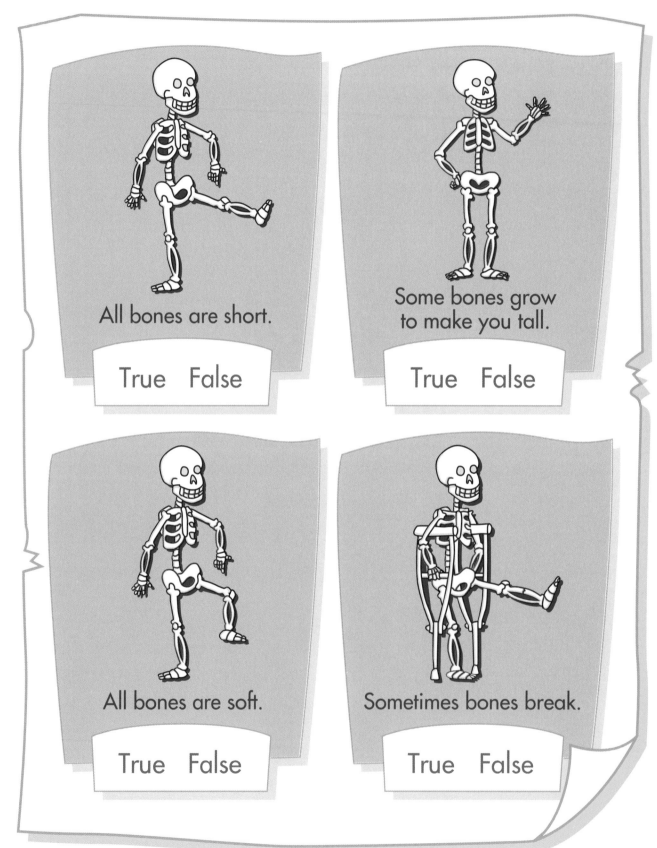

All bones are short.

True   False

Some bones grow to make you tall.

True   False

All bones are soft.

True   False

Sometimes bones break.

True   False

Look at the pictures.
Check the correct words to finish the sentences.
Write the words. Read the sentences.

My skeleton keeps my body
_____ .

☐ short and long

☐ big and good

☐ straight and strong

My _____ keeps my body
_____ and _____ .

My skeleton is good for me.
Without him, I'd be like _____ .

☐ candy

☐ jelly

☐ ice cream

My _____ is _____ for me.
_____ him, I'd be _____ _____ .

My bones are very_____ ,
with joints to help my body move.

☐ hard and smooth

☐ hard and soft

☐ soft and small

My _____ are very _____ and _____ ,
with joints to help my _____ _____ .

45

Play the game.

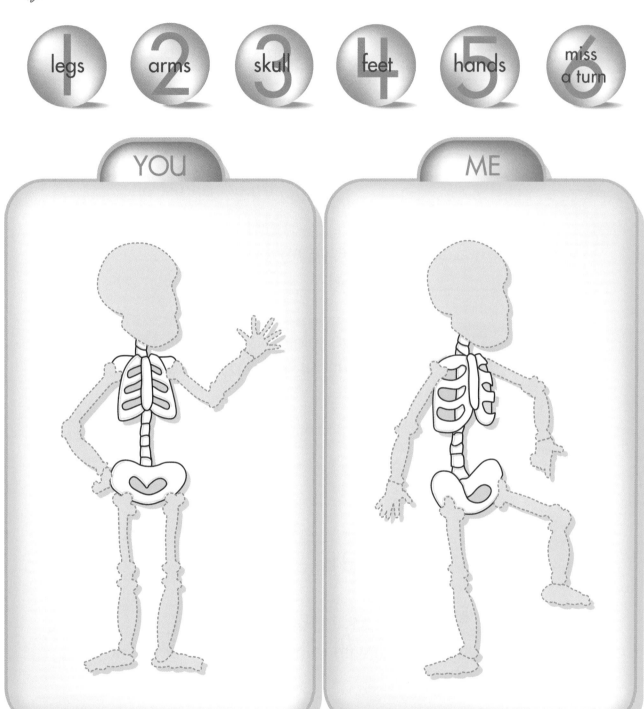

1 legs 2 arms 3 skull 4 feet 5 hands 6 miss a turn

YOU

ME

You need: number cube, stickers
1. Decide who goes first. Choose your board.
2. Look at the words that go with each number.
3. Throw the number cube. Stick a sticker on the bone that matches the number on the cube. Say, "My _____." If you throw a 6 you miss a turn.
4. The first player to stick on all the bones is the winner.

46

 Stick the stickers in the word boxes.
Write the words to finish the sentences.
Say the sentences.

b

g

fr

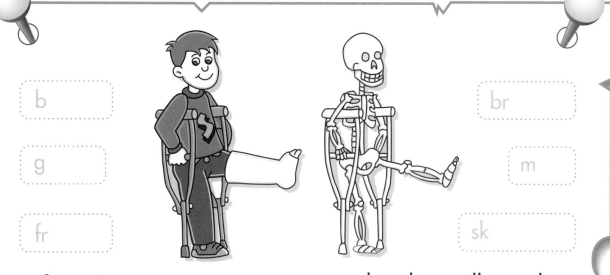

br

m

sk

Sometimes _____ _____ but they will mend.

My _____ is _____ to _____ .

My skeleton is my _____ .

sk

sk

h

i

f

My _____ is _____ my _____

and I am very _____ of _____ .

47

 Write the words. Use the Word Bank.
Say the sentences.

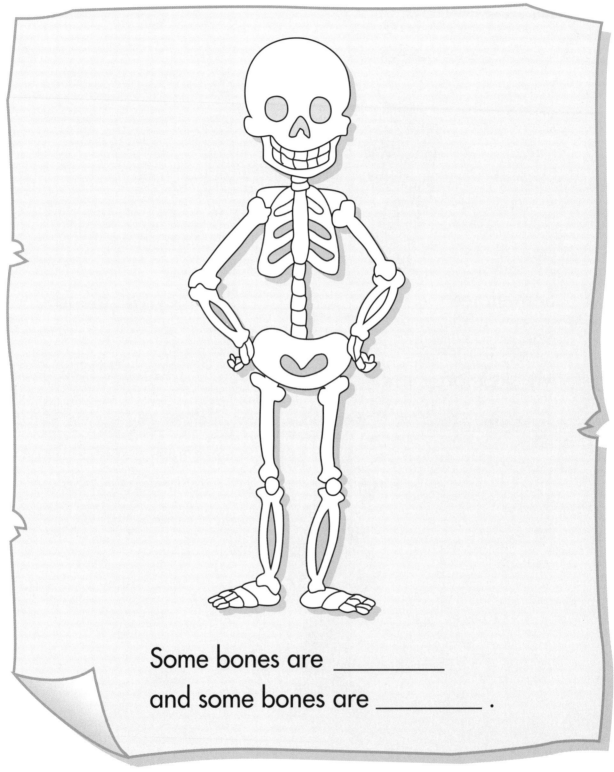

Some bones are _____

and some bones are _____ .

Word Bank   long   short

48

 Write the words to label the pictures.
Use the Word Bank. Write the words. Read the words.

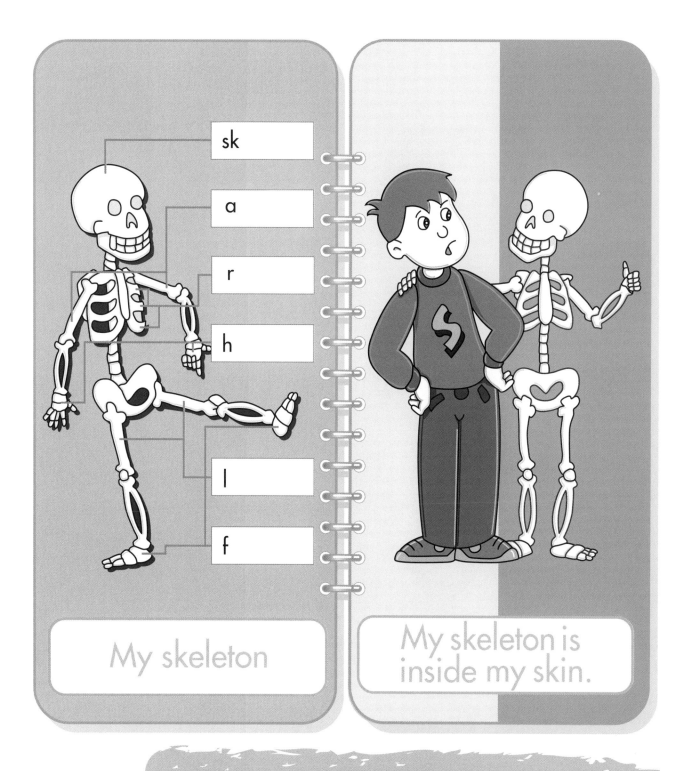

sk

a

r

h

l

f

My skeleton

My skeleton is
inside my skin.

Word Bank   legs   arms   ribs   hands   feet   skull

49

 How do joints help your body move? Trace the words. Match the words and pictures. Finish the sentence. Say the sentence.

bending
touching

lifting

talking

My bones have joints to help my body move.

Chewing____, l_____, wr_____, w_____,
j_____, b_____, t_____, t_____!

writing

jumping
chewing

walking

Stick the stickers to label the pictures.

m

g

s

c

d

v

j

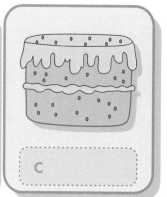

z

o

e

r

f

w

h

i

a

51

Sticker Sheet 5

 Stick the stickers.
Write the words to label the pictures.

w_____

a_____

o_____

s_____

g_____

v_____

c_____

f_____

e_____

d_____

j_____

m_____

r_____

i_____

h_____

z_____

Learnalot

Read *Learnalot*. Stick the stickers.
Write the words to label the pictures.
Use the Word Bank. Say the words.

E_____   L_____   I_____

or it
at

s_____ _____   n_____

b__ _____   s_____

Word Bank   Earth   numbers   small words
letters   big words   Learnalot   stories

54

Stick the stickers.
Match the pictures and sentences.
Write the letters in the circles.

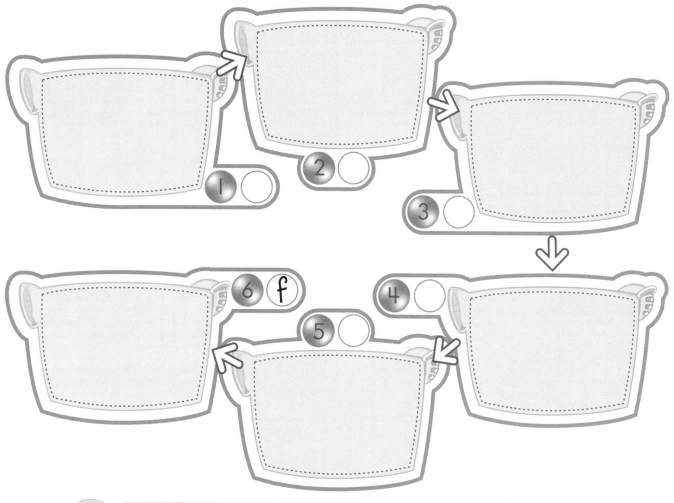

1 ○

2 ○

3 ○

6 (f)

5 ○

4 ○

(a) We learned how to make big words.

(b) We learned about numbers.

(c) We learned about letters.

(d) We learned how to read stories.

(e) We leaned how to make small words.

(f) We made lots of friends.

55

Stick the stickers to label the pictures.

b

k

l

a

n

p

q

t

u

x

y

c

e

f

m

v

56

 Read the words. Answer the questions.
Write the words. Use the Word Bank. Say the sentences.

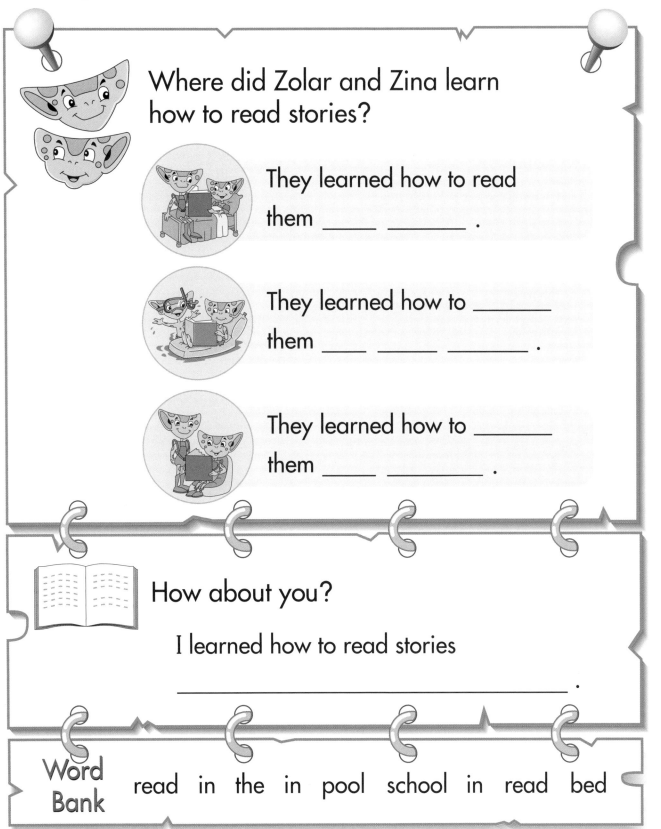

Where did Zolar and Zina learn
how to read stories?

They learned how to read
them ____ _____ .

They learned how to _____
them ____ ____ _____ .

They learned how to _____
them ____ _____ .

How about you?

I learned how to read stories

_____ .

Word
Bank   read   in   the   in   pool   school   in   read   bed

Look at the pictures. Read the words.
Circle True or False.

Earth

Zolar and Zina went
to visit Earth.

True   False

dinosaur

Zolar and Zina learned
how to make small words.

True   False

Zolar and Zina learned
how to read stories.

True   False

Zolar and Zina learned
about numbers.

True   False

 Play the game.

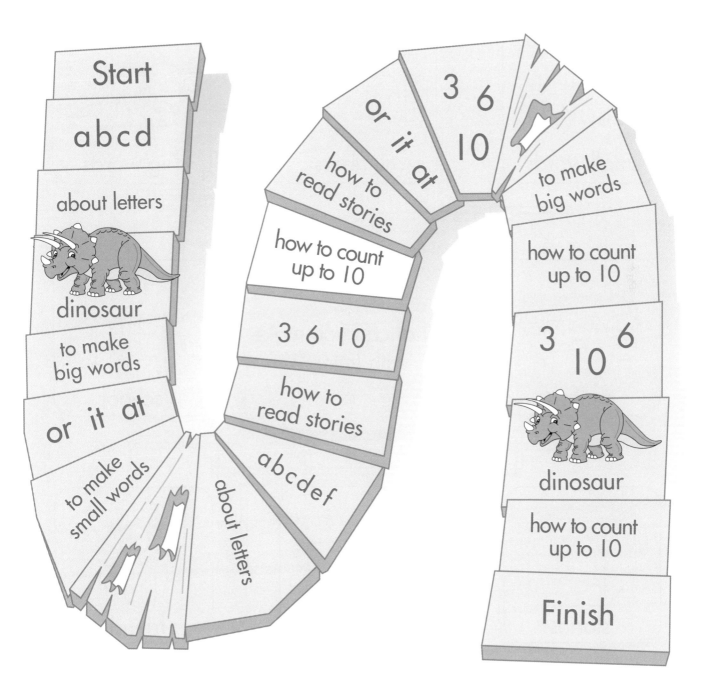

You need: counters, number cube

1. Make two teams and decide who goes first. Put two counters on **Start.**
2. Take turns throwing the number cube. Move the counter the same number of spaces.
   Say a sentence using the words from the space you land on.
   For example, "We learned how to make small words."
3. If you land on a space with a hole, miss a turn.
4. The first team to reach **Finish** is the winner.

What can you make with letters?
Look at the pictures. Write the words in the spaces.
Say the answers.

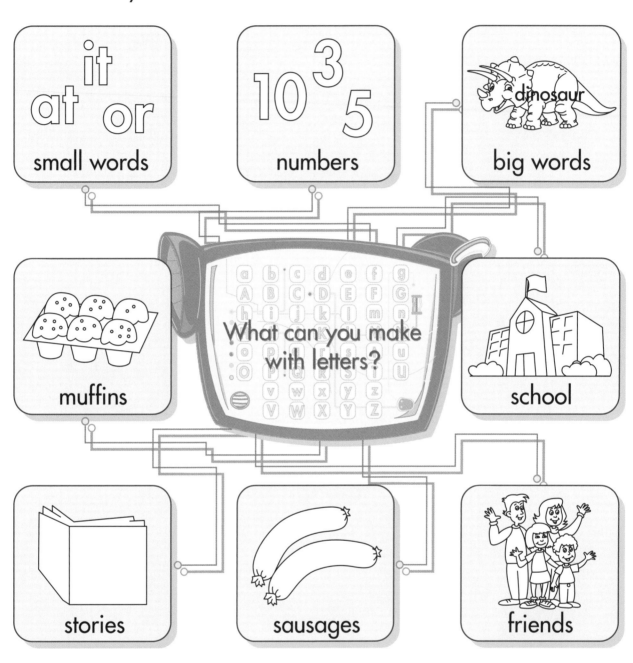

small words

numbers

dinosaur
big words

muffins

What can you make with letters?

school

stories

sausages

friends

We can make _____ _____ with letters.

We can make _____ _____ with letters.

We can make _____ with letters.

 Stick the stickers. Write labels for the pictures.
See page 56 to help you.

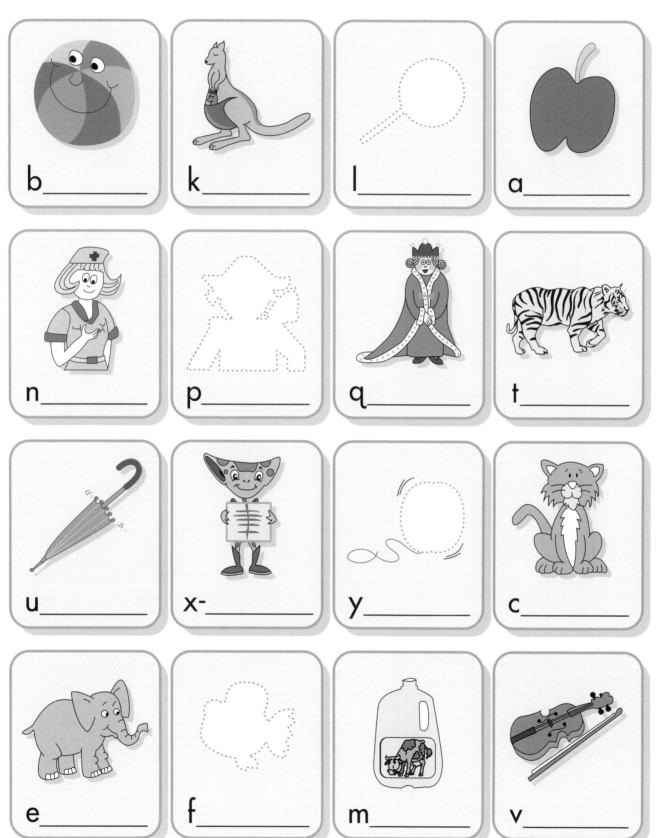

b_____

k_____

l_____

a_____

n_____

p_____

q_____

t_____

u_____

x-_____

y_____

c_____

e_____

f_____

m_____

v_____

61

Sticker Sheet 6

Read the questions.
Stick the stickers. Write the words.
Say the words and sentence.

Where do Zolar
and Zina live?

L _ _ _ _ _ _ _ _

Where do
you live?

E _ _ _ _ _

Why do Zolar and
Zina want to go
back to Earth?

They made lots of
fr_ _ _ _ _ _.

62

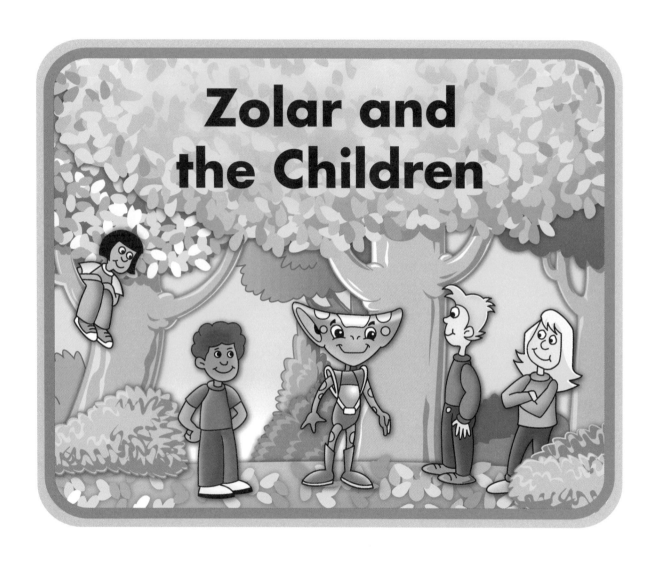

Zolar and the Children

63

 Read *Zolar and the Children*. Look at each picture.
Write the missing word.
Stick the sticker. Say the sentence.

"Can I _____ too?"
Zolar said.

"Shut your eyes
and _____
to twenty."

"_____ your eyes."

64

Look at the pictures. Read the words.
Stick the stickers. Say the sentences.

She cried

_____ .

She smiled

_____ .

65

Sticker Sheet 7

See the words beginning with **ch-**? Stick the stickers. Write the words. Say the words.

ch-

___ick

__impanzee

___eetah

ch

___ildren

___eese

___ocolate

66

Look at the pictures.
Read the words.
Circle True or False.

Zolar saw the children
playing leap-frog.

True   False

"The children don't want
to play with me,"
Zolar said sadly.

True   False

"Let's play a new game.
What about leap-frog?"

True   False

"I like leap-frog,"
said Zolar.

True   False

67

Stick the stickers on the pictures.
Write the words to finish the sentences.
Say the sentences.

seek

hide

children

Zolar saw the _____
playing _____-and-_____.

play

game

leap-frog

"Let's _____ a new _____.
What about _____?"

Sticker Sheet 7

Stick the stickers to label the games.
Say, "Let's play…"

"Let's play…"

69

Sticker Sheet 7

 Count and write the numbers.
Say the numbers from 1 to 10.

four

two

ten

eight

six

⑩ _____

⑨ nine

⑧ _____

⑦ seven

⑥ _____

⑤ five

④ _____

③ three

② _____

① one

70

 Play the game.

You need: stickers, number cube

1. Choose your board. Stick the stickers together to make six counters each.
2. Put the counters on your board with the question mark up. Don't let the other player see the other side of the counters.
3. Decide who goes first. Throw the number cube. Look at the picture on the other player's board with that number on it. Say, "Can I play _____?" The other player turns over their counter. If it is a smiley face, they say, "Yes." If it is a sad face, they say, "No."
4. The first player to turn over three smiley faces on the other player's board is the winner.

Look at the number and picture clues.
Find and circle the words in the puzzle.
Write the words in the boxes. Say the words.

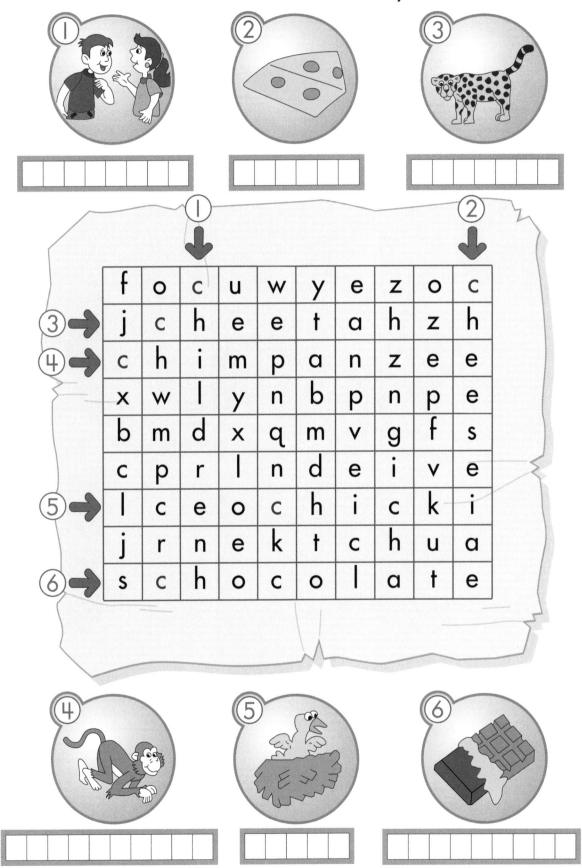

What Shall We Call the Kitten?

73

 Look at the letter and number. Find the picture on the chart. Write the word. Say the word.
Use the Word Bank.

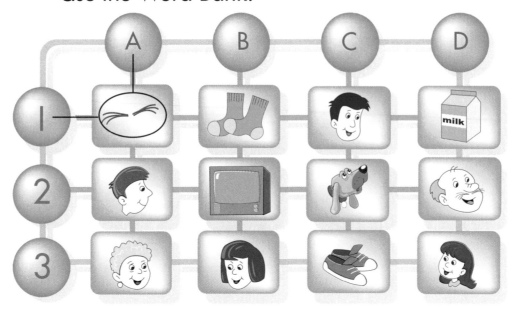

A1 ___whiskers___

A2 _____

A3 _____

B1 _____

B2 _____

B3 _____

C1 _____

C2 _____

C3 _____

D1 _____

D2 _____

D3 _____

Word Bank

Mom   Dad   Grandpa   Grandma   milk   shoes
socks   television   David   Amanda   dog   whiskers

74

"What shall we call the kitten?"
Stick the kitten name next to the person who suggested it.
Say, "I think we should call him…"

Slurper

Weghopi

Whiskers

Pet Store

TV

Socks

Nuisance

75

Sticker Sheet 8

What does the kitten like doing?
Look at the pictures. Read the words.
Stick a smiley sticker next to the things he likes.

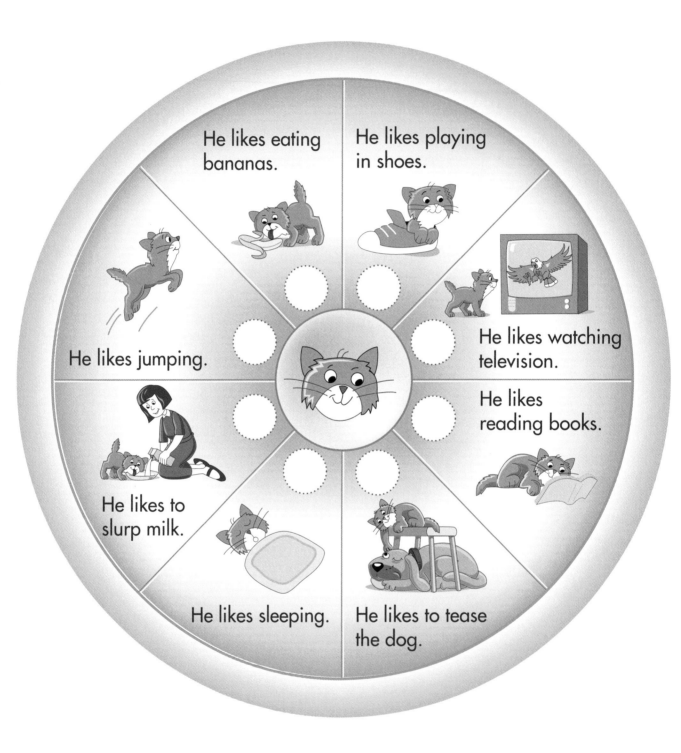

He likes eating bananas.

He likes playing in shoes.

He likes jumping.

He likes watching television.

He likes reading books.

He likes to slurp milk.

He likes sleeping.

He likes to tease the dog.

76

Play the game.

1	2	3	4	5	6
Dad	Grandpa	Amanda	David	Mom	Grandma

You

TV	Socks	Nuisance
Whiskers	TV	Socks
Weghopi	Slurper	Weghopi
Nuisance	Whiskers	Slurper

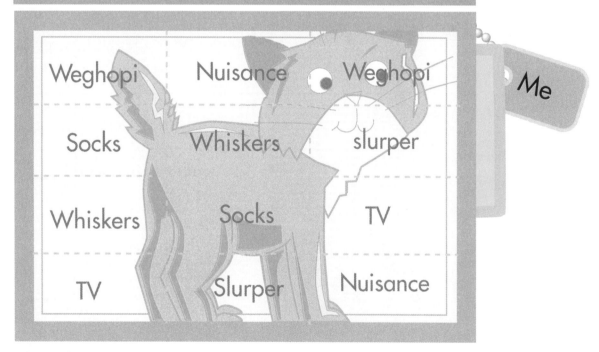

Weghopi	Nuisance	Weghopi
Socks	Whiskers	slurper
Whiskers	Socks	TV
TV	Slurper	Nuisance

Me

You need: number cube, stickers

1. Decide who goes first. Choose your board.
2. Throw the number cube. Match the number on the number cube with the person and find out what he/she wants to call the kitten. Stick the name sticker on your board.
   Say, "I think I will call him _____," said _____.
3. The first player to cover their board with stickers is the winner.

77

Sticker Sheet 8

Color the pictures that begin with **wh-**.
Write the words.
Label the **wh-** words in the picture.
Say the words.

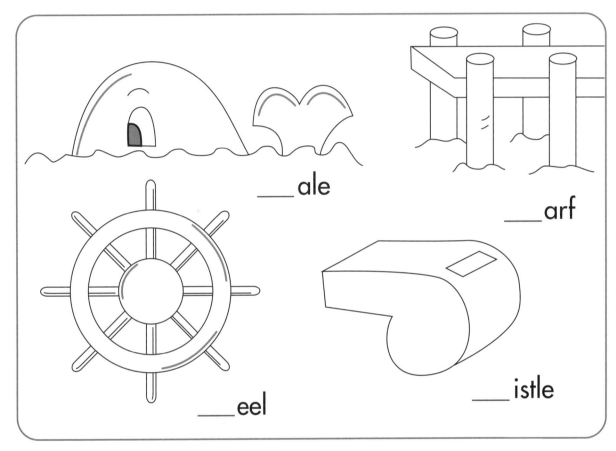

___ale

___arf

___eel

___istle

wh _____

wh _____

wh _____

Color the balloons that have words beginning with **wh-**.
Write the words in the boxes.
Say the words.

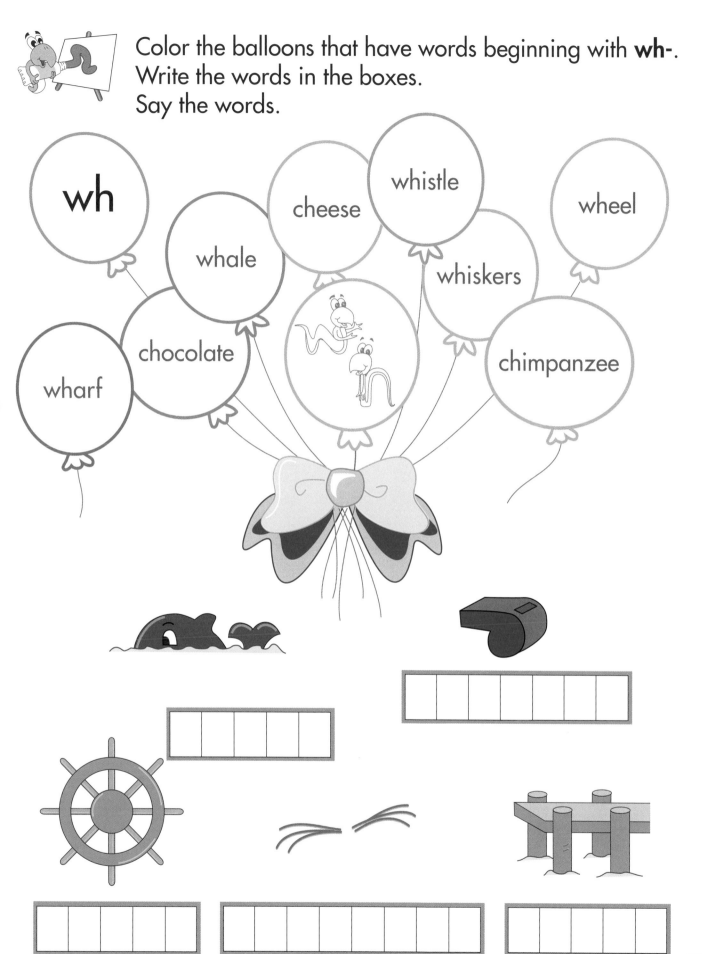

Stick the stickers on the pictures.
Read the words. Circle True or False.

"I think we should call him
TV because he likes
playing in shoes."

True   False

"I think we should call him
Slurper because he likes
to slurp his milk."

True   False

"I think we should call him
Whiskers because he likes
to tease the dog."

True   False

"I think the kitten wants to
call himself Weghopi!"

True   False

80

Sticker Sheet 8

© 2006 Wendy Pye Publishing Ltd

"What shall we call the kitten?"
Write the words each person says. Use the Word Bank.
Say the words.

We should call him...

Socks _____
he likes playing
in my _____ .

TV because
he _____ watching
_____ .

Slurper because
he _____ to slurp
his _____ .

Nuisance
_____ he likes to
tease the _____ .

Word Bank

likes   because   milk   dog   television
shoes   likes   because

What are Dad and Grandpa saying?
Look at the numbers and pictures.
Write the words. Say the sentences.

think   Whiskers

Grandpa

should

like

me

call

because

whiskers

call

shall

Dad

kitten

What

1

"Wh_____ sh_____ we c_____ the

k_____?" said D_____ .

2

"I th_____ we sh_____ c_____ him

Wh_____," said Gr_____,

"b_____ he's got wh_____ just _____ _____ ."

The Bungee Jump

 Read *The Bungee Jump*. Read the questions. Check the answer. Write the words to label the picture. Use the Word Bank.

| Who looked at the water? | ☐ Mom
☐ the man |

| Who counted 5, 4, 3, 2, 1, jump? | ☐ Mom
☐ the man |

| Who went up and down, up and down? | ☐ Mom
☐ the man |

| Did Mom want to jump again? | ☐ Yes, she did.
☐ No, she didn't. |

Word Bank   high bridge   Mom's ankles   strap   Mom

84

Say the words. Color the pictures in each row that begin with the same sound.

skeleton	frog	skates	skip
clown	clock	spider	clouds
flag	flowers	flute	grapes
swans	dress	swing	swimmer

Look at the number clues.
Write the words in the boxes.
Use the Word Bank.

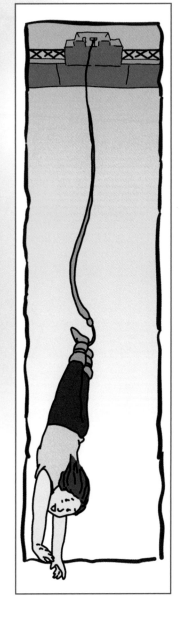

Across
1. What is the first number of the countdown (page 4)?
2. Where did the man tie the strap (page 2)?
3. What was around Mom's ankles (page 2)?

Down
4. How did Mom get off the bridge (page 6)?
5. What did Mom jump off (page 6)?
6. What was under the bridge (page 2)?

Word Bank   strap five water ankles jumped bridge

86

Stick the stickers to make the picture.
Write the words to finish the sentences.
Use the Word Bank.

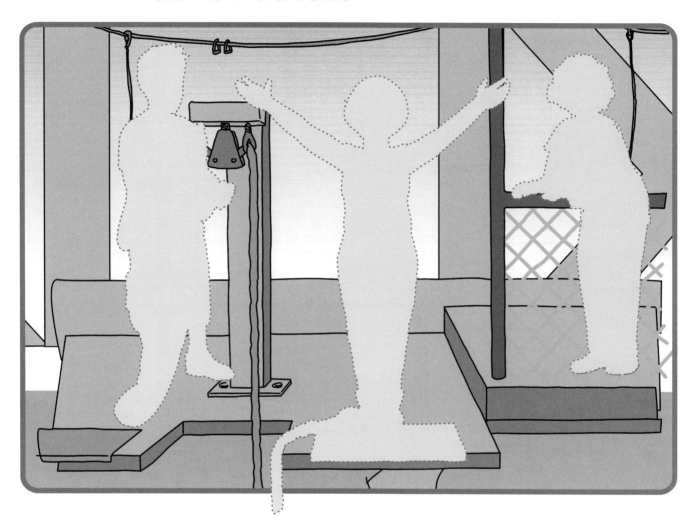

"I _____ to jump!" Mom _____.

"Are you _____?" _____ the man.

"Five, _____ , three, _____ , one…

_____!"

Word Bank   jump   want   ready   two   said   four   asked

Sticker Sheet 9

Finish the number patterns.
Write the missing numbers.

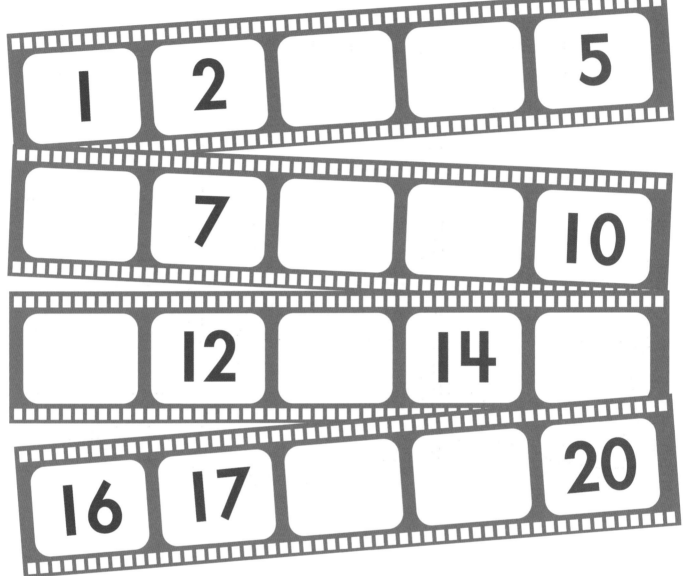

| 1 | 2 | | | 5 |

| | 7 | | | 10 |

| | 12 | | 14 | |

| 16 | 17 | | | 20 |

Count the pictures and write the number.

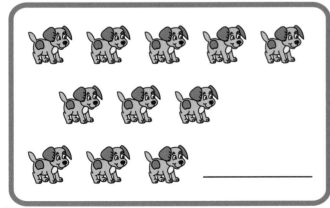

Stick the stickers on the picture to make labels.
Write Mom's words in the speech bubble.

Look at the numbers and picture clues.
Write the words in the boxes. Use the Word Bank.

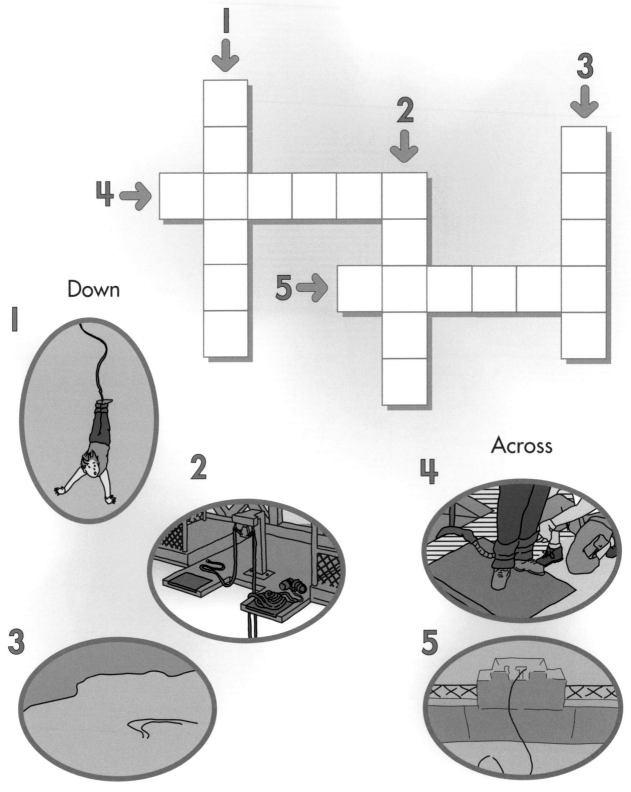

Down

Across

Word Bank   bridge   bungee   strap   water   ankles

Match the word with its opposite.
Write the words to finish the sentence.

down •   • whispered

above •   • below

long •   • up

yelled •   • short

Then she went ___ and _____ ,
___ and _____ .

What comes next?
Use the Word Bank to finish the sentences.

The man tied a strap _____ _____ _____ .

Mom hopped onto _____ _____ _____ .

She looked at ___ _____ ___ _____ _____ .

It was ___ _____ , _____ _____ _____ .

Word Bank

a long, long way down

the water way down below

around Mom's ankles

the high bridge

92

Little Duck's Walk

Read *Little Duck's Walk.* Where did Little Duck go on her walk? Write the words. Use the Word Bank. Draw the line.

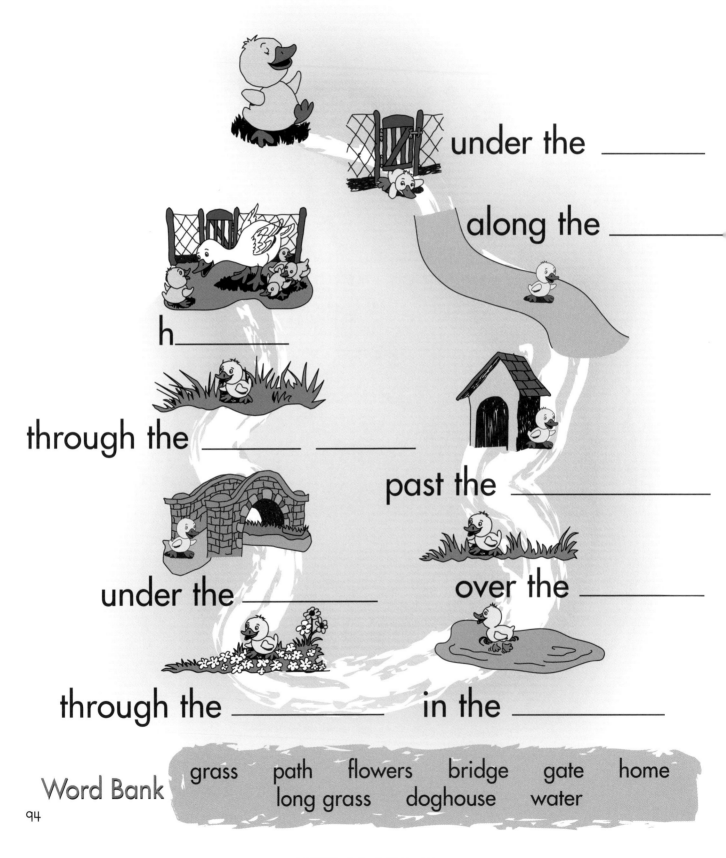

under the _____

along the _____

h_____

through the _____ _____

past the _____

under the _____

over the _____

through the _____

in the _____

Word Bank

grass   path   flowers   bridge   gate   home
long grass   doghouse   water

Spell the words for Word Slurper.
Write the words. Say the words.

w_____

wh_____   t____

a____   c_____

s_____

said

am

the

what

can

went

Say the words. Color the pictures in each row that begin with the same sound.

truck	tree	flower	tractor
star	sticks	stones	drum
frog	crab	fridge	fruit
spoon	spacecraft	glasses	spider

Read Little Duck's Walk.
Read the clues below and write the words.

Across
1. How did Little Duck swim on page 5?
2. How did Little Duck get into the water on page 4?
3. What did Little Duck walk under on page 7?
4. Where was Little Duck on page 8?

Down
5. What did Little Duck go for on page 5?
6. Little Duck went _____ the gate on page 2.
7. What did Little Duck walk past on page 3?

Stick the stickers to label the pictures.
Write the words to finish the sentences.

Little Duck walked past the _____ .

She walked over the _____ .

She got out of the _____ .

She walked through the _____ .

98

Where did Little Duck walk? Use the Word Bank.
Write the words.
Draw the pictures.

_____ the gate

_____ the path

_____ the doghouse

_____ the grass

_____ the flowers

_____ the bridge

_____ the long grass

Word Bank over   through   through   under   under   past   along

99

Look at each picture.
What sound does the word begin with? Say the sound.
Write the letters. Say the word.

gr-	fl-	br-

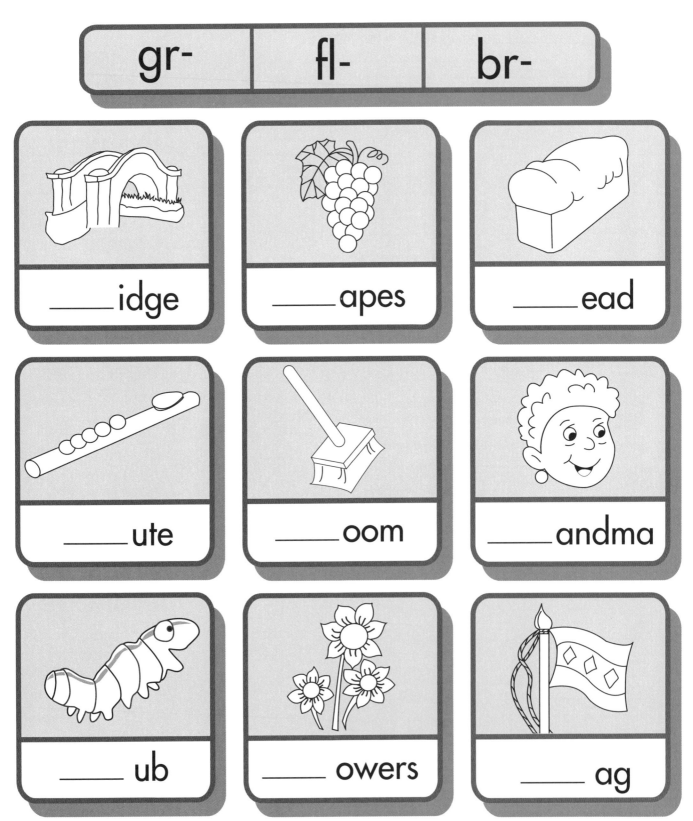

_____idge

_____apes

_____ead

_____ute

_____oom

_____andma

_____ub

_____owers

_____ag

Stick the stickers in the word bank.
Make sentences to match the pictures.
Write the words. Say the sentences.

Word Bank

Little _____ _____ _____ _____ _

_____ _____ _____ _____ _

Word Bank

_ I'm _____ _____ ___ _

_____ _____ _____ _

Sticker Sheet 10

 Stick the stickers. Use the Word Bank.
Write the sentences.

"What a good _____ I am!

I can _____ fast," said Little _____ .

"What lovely _____," said _____ Duck.

Word Bank   swim   Duck   swimmer   flowers   Little

102

Yummy in My Tummy

Read *Yummy in My Tummy*.
Read the words. Check True or False.

Mom wants help to make a cake.

True ☐ False ☐

Zac and Tilly want to help Mom make a cake.

True ☐ False ☐

Zac likes making cakes.

True ☐ False ☐

Tilly likes eating cakes.

True ☐ False ☐

Zac and Tilly want to eat cake.

True ☐ False ☐

The cake has lots of colors.

True ☐ False ☐

The cake looks like a butterfly.

True ☐ False ☐

The cake will fly into Zac's tummy.

True ☐ False ☐

Stick the stickers to show what the characters are saying. Write the sentence.

"Who will _____ me _____ a cake?"

Sticker Sheet 11

Write the words that rhyme. Use the Word Bank.

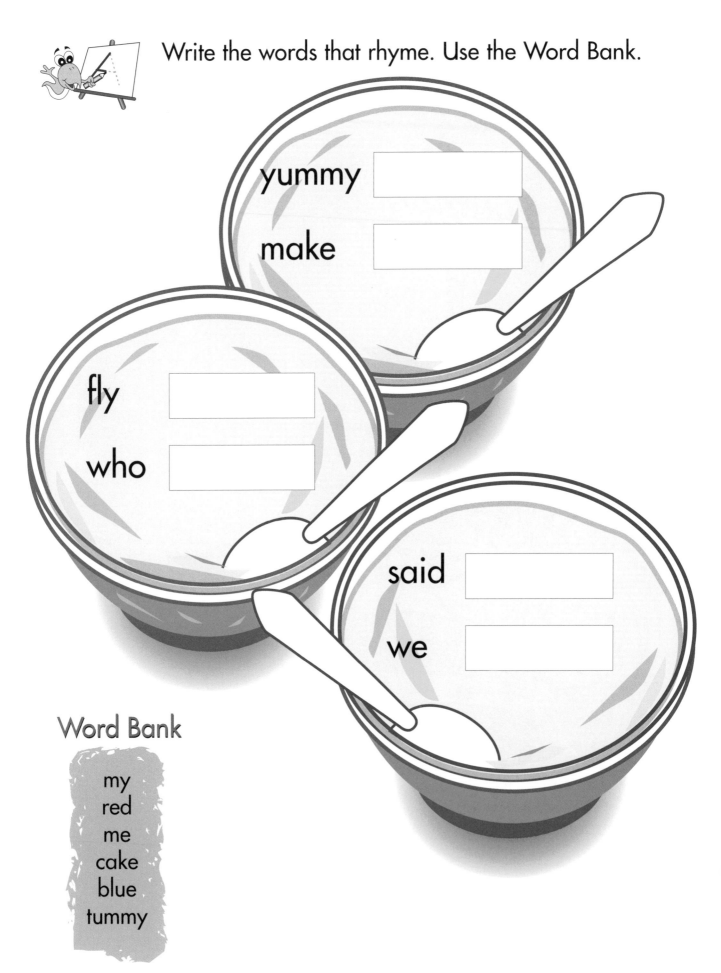

yummy _____

make _____

fly _____

who _____

said _____

we _____

Word Bank

my
red
me
cake
blue
tummy

Stick the stickers to match the color words.
Color the picture using these colors.
Write a sentence about the cake.

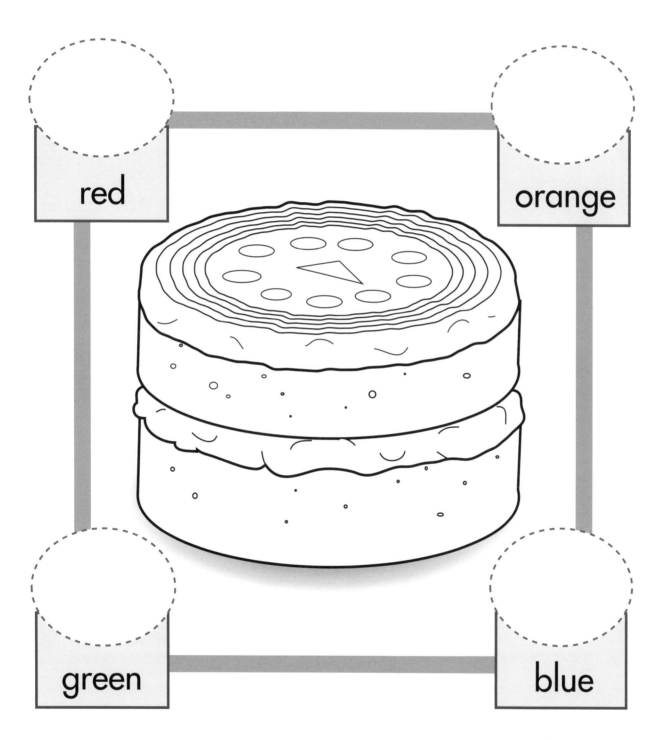

red

orange

green

blue

My cake is _____ and _____ .

Sticker Sheet 11

Play the game and make a recipe for something yummy in your tummy.

You need: stickers, number cube

1. Stick the stickers together to make counters. Put your counters on **Start**.
2. Each player will need a piece of paper and a pencil. Write **Recipe** at the top of the paper.
3. Decide who goes first. Throw the number cube and move the counter the number of squares.
4. When you land on a square, read out the words and write them on your paper.
5. Take turns to throw the number cube and write your recipes until everyone has reached **Finish**.
6. Read your recipes. Are they yummy?

Look at the pictures. Read the words.
Check the correct words to finish the sentence.
Write the words to finish the sentence.

The cake will look like

_____ .

○ a rocket
○ a butterfly
○ a tummy

The cake _____ .

○ is a butterfly
○ smells good
○ looks good

We'll have _____ .

○ red and green cake
○ lots of cake
○ lots of colors

Stick the icing on the cake.
Use the Word Bank.
Write the sentences to match.

This cake is a _____ .
It has _____ and _____ icing.

This cake is a _____ .
It has _____ and _____ icing.

Word Bank

butterfly   orange   red   green
blue   rocket   hippo   yellow

This cake is a _____ .
It has _____ icing.

Say the words. Color the pictures in each row that begin with the same sound.

| **pl**ane | **fl**ag | **pl**um | **pl**ate |

| **br**oom | **br**ead | **tr**uck | **br**idge |

| **dr**um | **cl**oud | **dr**ess | **dr**ip |

| **cr**ab | **cr**ocodile | **gr**apes | **cr**own |

111

 Number the pictures in the order of the story.
Write the sentences. Use the Word Bank.

Word Bank

icing
making
butterfly
looks
top

① I like _____ cakes.

② The cake _____ good.

③ I have to put the _____ on _____ .

④ The cake will look like a _____ .

Turtle Eggs

Read *Turtle Eggs*.
Look at the pictures.
Write the captions.

_____

_____

_____

_____

"Baby turtles come out of eggs."   Jack saw a book about turtles.

"There are no turtles in the eggs."   Jack got out an egg and broke it.

114

 Stick the stickers to show what the characters are saying. Write the sentences. Use the Word Bank.

Word Bank   baby   library   book   eggs   mom   turtles

Jack went to the _____ with his _____.

He saw a _____ about _____.

Jack liked the _____ turtles coming out of the _____ .

115

Sticker Sheet 12

Play the game.

You need: stickers, number cube

1. Look at the animals on the board and find out which ones come from eggs and which ones don't.
2. Stick the stickers to make counters.
3. Decide who goes first. Put your counters on **Start**.
4. Throw the number cube and move the counter the same number of squares.
5. Say the name of the animal. If the animal comes from an egg, have another turn.
   If it doesn't come from an egg, miss a turn.
6. The winner is the first player to reach **Finish**.

116

Read the words. Look at the picture.
Check the correct words. Write a sentence to match.
Say the words.

Jack saw
- ( ) a book about fridges.
- ( ) a book about turtles.
- ( ) a book about ducks.

_____ saw a book about_____ .

Jack's dad looked at
- ( ) the fridge.
- ( ) the turtles.
- ( ) the eggs.

Jack's _____ looked at the eggs and _____ at Jack.

He _____ ____ _____
and looked in.
- ( ) opened the fridge
- ( ) opened the door
- ( ) opened the egg

_____ opened the door and _____ in.

117

Read the numbers and words.
Stick the stickers to match.

1

2

3

4

1 Jack went to the library with his mom.

2 Jack took the book home and showed his dad.

3 The next day, Jack went to the fridge.

4 Soon all the eggs were broken.

118

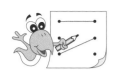

Help the turtle get to the sea.
Draw a line all the way.

Say the words. Color the pictures in each row that begin with the same sound.

gloves	glasses	glue	star
smoke	plane	smile	smell
grapes	grasshopper	grass	clock
snake	snail	tree	snow

 Draw a picture. Write sentences for your pictures.

 Baby turtles come out of eggs.

Baby birds come out of eggs.

Baby _____ come out of eggs.

Baby _____ come out of eggs.

121

Write labels for the pictures. Start with these words: gloves, glasses, glue, star. See page 116 to help you.

gl

gl

gl

st

sm

pl

sm

sm

gr

gr

gr

cl

sn

sn

tr

sn

It's for You

Read *It's For You.* Then read the words.
Circle True or False.

"I'm talking to
an octopus about
tomatoes," said Sandy.

True   False

"I'm talking to a shark
about shopping,"
said Sandy.

True   False

"I'm talking to a shark
about shopping,"
said Sandy.

True   False

"I'm talking to
an octopus about
orangutans," said Sandy.

True   False

Color the words that begin with **sh-**.
Write the words in the boxes.
Say the words.

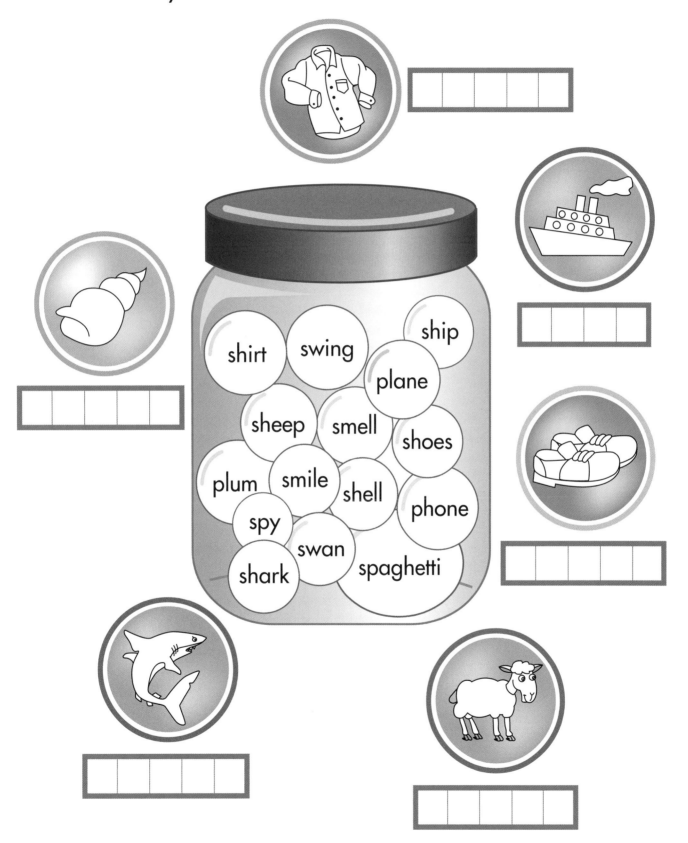

Stick the stickers to show what the characters are saying. Write the sentences. Use the Word Bank.

"Wh___ are you _____ ?" asked ____ .

"I'm using my sh_____ ph_____,"

said _____ .

Read the questions. Write the answers. Use the Word Bank.

What did Dad do when Sandy said she was using her shell phone?

Dad _____ .

Where did Sandy put the shell phone?

She held it to _____ _____ .

What did Sandy write in the sand?

"It's _____ _____ ."

Word Bank   laughed   her ear   4 U

127

 Stick the stickers. Write the labels.
Use the Word Bank.

_____

_____

_____

_____

Word Bank   shark   dolphin   turtle   octopus

Match the words that start with the same letter or sound.

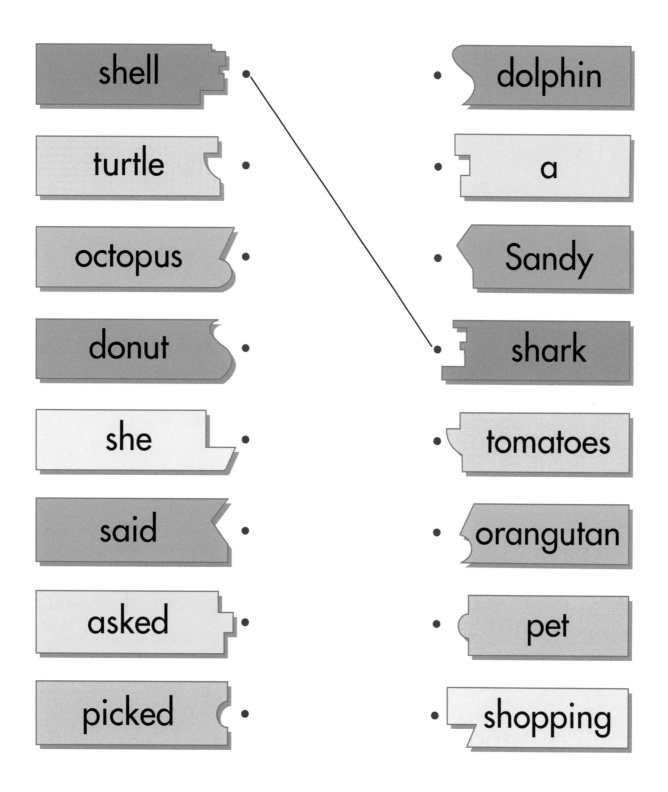

shell

turtle

octopus

donut

she

said

asked

picked

dolphin

a

Sandy

shark

tomatoes

orangutan

pet

shopping

129

Stick the stickers in the word bank.
Write the words to finish the sentences.
Say the sentences.

Word Bank

"Who are you _____ to _____?"
asked Dad.

"I'm not _____ to _____,"
said _____ .

"I'm sending a _____ _____ .

It's for _____!"

Sticker Sheet 13

© 2006 Wendy Pye Publishing Ltd

Play the game.

You need: stickers, number cube
1. Stick the stickers to make counters.
2. Decide who goes first. Put your counters on **Start**.
3. Throw the number cube and move the counter the number of squares.
4. When you land on a square say, "I'm talking to a _____ about _____." Make sure you say a word that starts with the same letter as the animal. For example, "I'm talking to a parrot about pancakes."
5. If you can't think of a word, miss a turn.
6. The first player to reach **Finish** is the winner.

131

Sticker Sheet 13

Write a sentence for each picture. Use the Word Bank.

I'm talking to

a _____

about _____ .

I'm talking to

a _____

about _____ .

I'm talking to

an _____

about _____ .

Word Bank

| turtle | octopus | donuts |
| orangutans | tomatoes | dolphin |

The Worst Haircut in the World

Read *The Worst Haircut in the World.*
Look at the picture. Read the words.
Check the correct sentence.

What was Sam's problem?

☐ He gave himself a haircut.

☐ He painted his hair green.

What did Sam think he could tell Mom?

☐ Grandpa borrowed his hair.

☐ Grandpa knitted his hair.

What did Sam say about Uncle Jed?

☐ Uncle Jed clipped his hair.

☐ Uncle Jed painted his hair green.

What did Sam really tell Mom?

☐ A goat ate his hair.

☐ The truth

Stick the stickers to match the captions.

It was the worst haircut in the world.

I could tell Mom that Grandpa borrowed my hair.

I could tell Mom that Grandma knitted my hair.

I could tell Mom that Aunt Sue painted my hair green.

Then a goat ate it.

"I don't believe it!" Mom said.

135

Sticker Sheet 14

Stick the stickers next to the correct words.
Write the names in the speech bubbles.

I could tell Mom that
_____
painted my hair green.

I could tell Mom that
_____
borrowed my hair.

I could tell Mom that
_____
knitted my hair.

I could tell Mom that
_____
clipped my hair.

136

Find the letters on the chart to finish the words.
Write the letters. Say the words.

belie <u>v</u> __

hairc __ __

myse __ __

tru __ __

Spell the words for Word Slurper.

th____   t____

c____   g____   d____

w____

tell   that   don't

could   will   gave

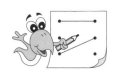

Match the words that rhyme.

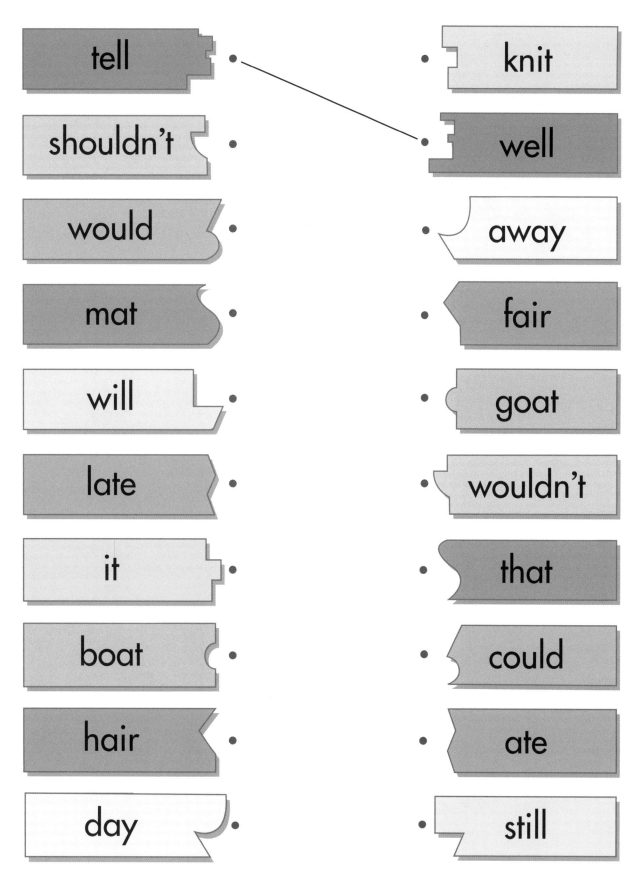

tell

shouldn't

would

mat

will

late

it

boat

hair

day

knit

well

away

fair

goat

wouldn't

that

could

ate

still

139

Look at the picture puzzles. Which word matches? Check the word. Say the word.

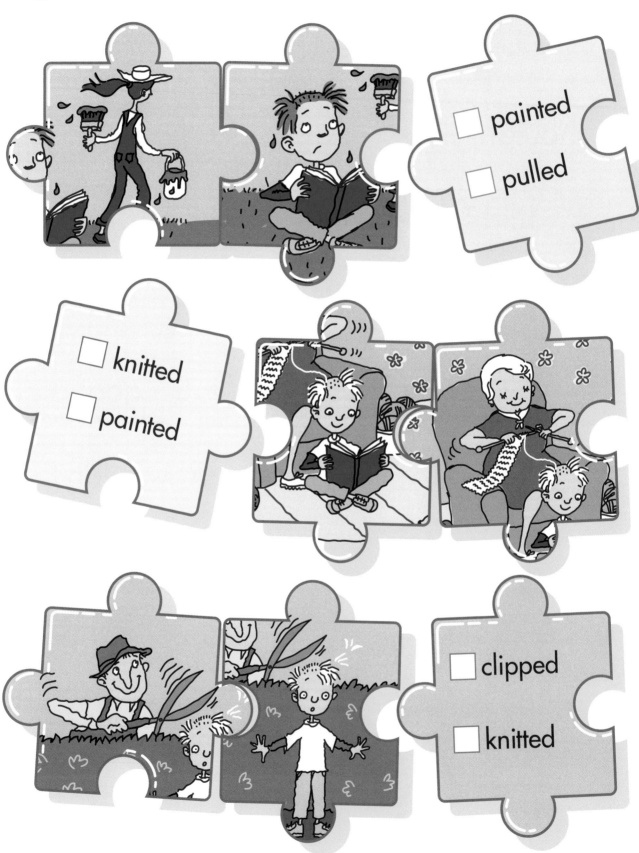

☐ painted

☐ pulled

☐ knitted

☐ painted

☐ clipped

☐ knitted

Play the game.

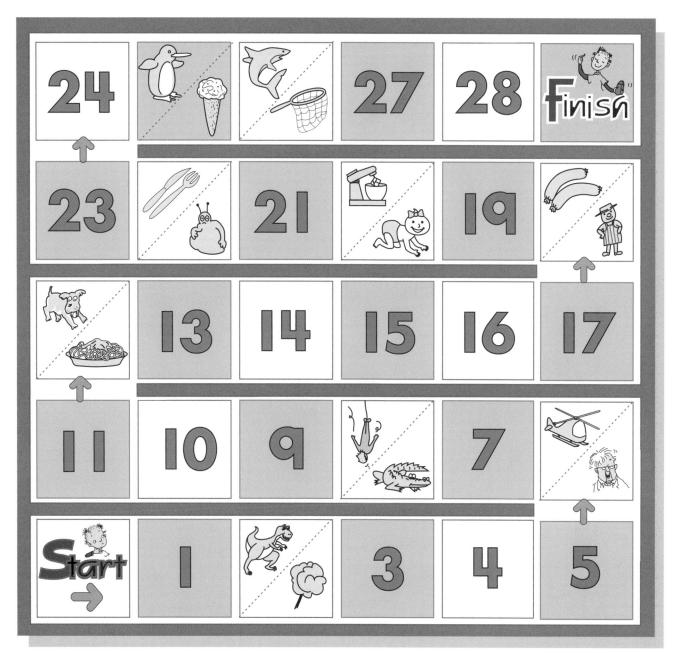

You need: stickers, number cube
1. Stick the stickers together to make counters.
2. Decide who goes first. Put your counters on **Start**.
3. Throw the number cube and move the counter the same number of squares.
4. If you land on a picture square, make an excuse for a bad haircut that uses the pictures in the square. For example, "The dinosaur thought I was a lollipop and ate my hair."
5. If you can't make an excuse, you miss a turn.
6. The first player to reach **Finish** is the winner.

What words begin with gr-? Stick the stickers.
Write the words. Say the words.

| gr- | ___ub | ___andpa | green
___een |
| gr- | ___apes | ___owl | ___in |

Stick the stickers to show what the people are saying.

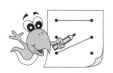

Match the words. Write the words.

flashes	sparkles	<u>sparkles</u>
man	finished	_____
finished	flashes	_____
people	beautiful	_____
beautiful	shouted	_____
when	sky	_____
more	moon	_____
sky	more	_____
fireworks	man	_____
shouted	look	_____
look	shine	_____
moon	fireworks	_____
sparkles	people	_____
shine	when	_____

145

Read the sentences. Use the Word Bank.
Write the words in the speech balloons.

Word Bank

Ooh! Aah!

Do you want more fireworks?

Are you ready?

146

Write the sentences to match the pictures.
Use the Word Bank.

_____

_____

_____

_____

_____

_____

_____

_____

_____

_____

_____

_____

Word Bank

The people went home.
The people went to see the fireworks.
The sky was bright with glitter and sparkles.
"Look at the sky!" shouted the people.

147

Play the game.

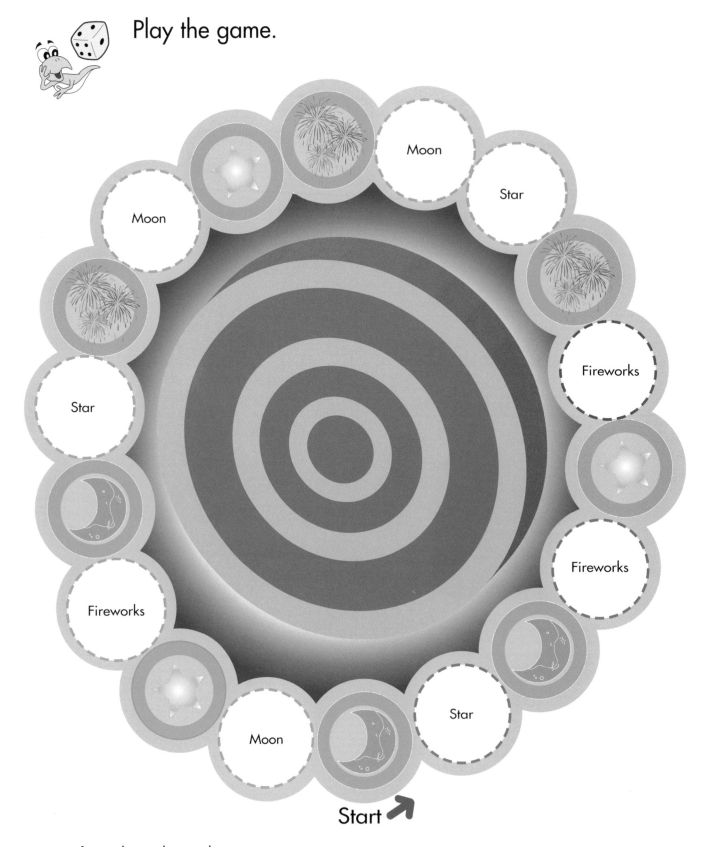

You need: number cube, stickers

1. Decide who goes first and throw the number cube. Move the number of circles on the number cube. If you land on star, moon, or fireworks, stick a sticker on it. If you land on a space with a sticker already there, miss a turn.

2. The player who sticks the most stickers is the winner.

148

Read the sentences.
Circle True or False.

The man was wearing gloves.

True   False

There were flashes.

True   False

There were bangs.

True   False

"Ooh! Aah!" The man said.

True   False

The people wanted more fireworks.

True   False

The sky was beautiful.

True   False

The moon was shining.

True   False

The stars were glittering.

True   False

149

Write the missing words in the sentences.
Use the Word Bank.

"Look at the _____," said the m_____.

There were more b_____.

"Ooh!"

There were more fl_____.

"Aah!"

Word Bank   flashes   bangs   man   sky

Put the quotation marks into the sentences.

Ooh!

Aah!

Look at the sky, shouted the people.

It is beautiful.

150

Look at the words in the word bank.
Write the naming words on the book.

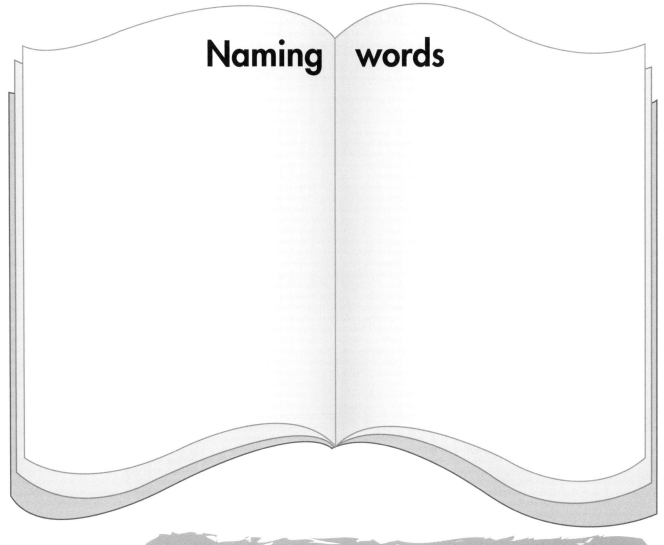

Naming   words

Word Bank

fireworks   people   flashes   with
bangs   sparkles   sky   stars
man   said   moon   glitter

Finish the sentences.

The people w_____ to see the f_____.

"Look at the sk___," sh_____ the p_____.

151

Read *Ooh! Aah!*
What do fireworks look like? Draw a picture.
What do fireworks sound like?
Write sound words on your picture.
Write about fireworks.

_____

_____

_____

_____

_____

152

The Roller Coaster Ride

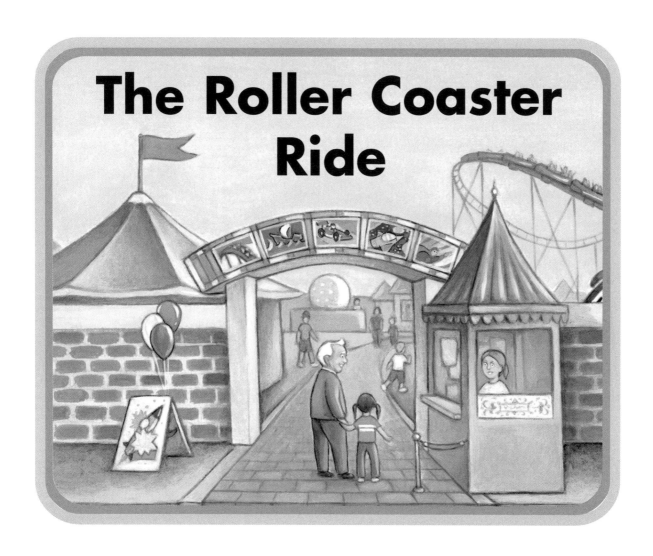

Read *The Roller Coaster Ride.*
Draw a picture of yourself going up and down,
over and under, or upside down.
Write a sentence about your picture.

I am going _____ .

154

Number the pictures in the right order. Write the sentences from the Word Bank that match the pictures.

_____

_____

_____

_____

_____

_____

1. "That looks like fun," said Grandad. "Will you come with me?"
2. "All right, you go on the roller coaster," said Marie.
3. Marie didn't think Grandad was having fun.
4. "No," said Grandad. "I didn't wave. I did feel sick."

155

Read *The Roller Coaster Ride.*
Look at the illustrations.

Draw what happened at the beginning of the story.

Draw what happened in the middle of the story.

Draw what happened at the end of the story.

156

 Match the words to make contractions. Write the words. Use the Word Bank.

would ——————— not		_wouldn't_
I	am	_____
I	will	_____
they	are	_____
can	not	_____
did	not	_____
do	not	_____
is	not	_____
they	will	_____

Word Bank

wouldn't they're can't I'll
they'll didn't I'm don't isn't

157

 Use the Word Bank to write the sentences.

The roller coaster went u___ and d_____ .

It went o_____ and u_____.

It even went u_____ d_____ .

"That looks l_____ fun," said Grandad.

"Will you come w_____me?"

"I am going f_____ a ride."

"Will you wave t____me?"

"No,"_____ Marie. "I_____ feel sick.

Word Bank

upside	under	down	with
down	would	for	like
over	up	said	to

 Stick the stickers to match the pictures.
Write the words.

The roller coaster went _____ and _____ .

It even went _____ _____ .

Sticker Sheet 15

All right, you go on
the roller coaster, said Marie.
I'll watch. Will you wave to me?

Of course I will, said Grandad.
I'll even wave when I'm
upside down.

No, said Grandad.
I didn't wave.
I did feel sick.
I didn't have fun.

 Write the words that need upper case letters in the boxes.

"all right, you go on the rollercoaster," said marie.

All

"of course I will," said grandad. "i'll even wave when i'm upside down."

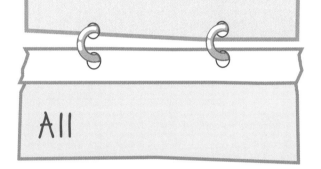

"i'll watch. will you wave to me?"

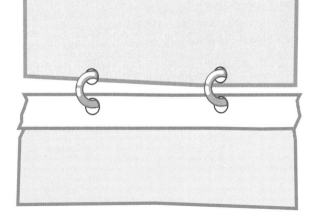

"grandad, you didn't wave," said marie.

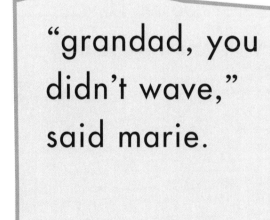

 Write in the speech bubbles what Grandad and Marie say. Use the Word Bank.

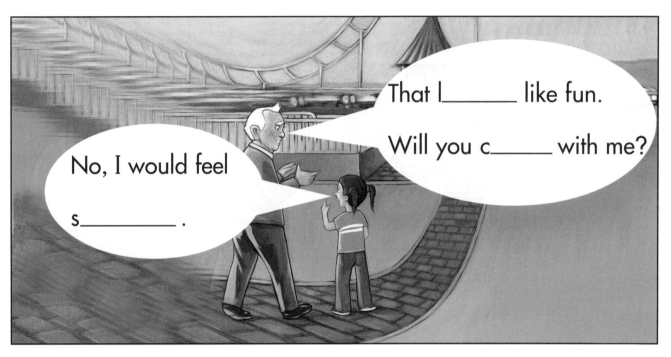

That l_____ like fun.

Will you c_____ with me?

No, I would feel s_____ .

All right, you g__ on the roller coaster. I'll w_____. Will you wave to me?

Of course I w_____ . I'll even w_____ when I'm upside down.

Word Bank wave   will   go   watch   looks   sick   come

Sticker Sheet 1

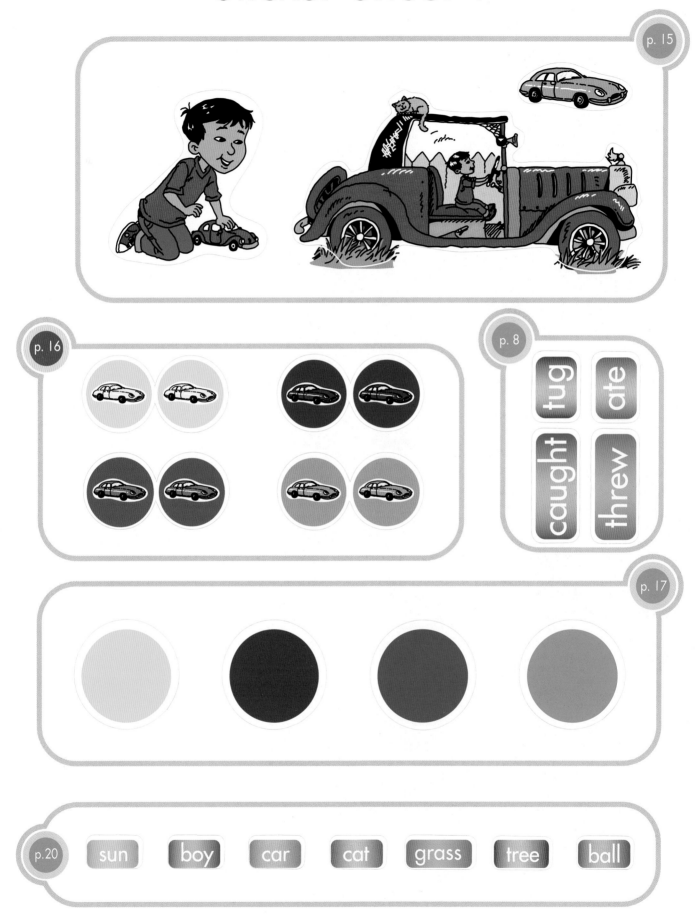

p. 15

p. 16

p. 8

tug ate

caught threw

p. 17

p.20 sun boy car cat grass tree ball

Sticker Sheet 2

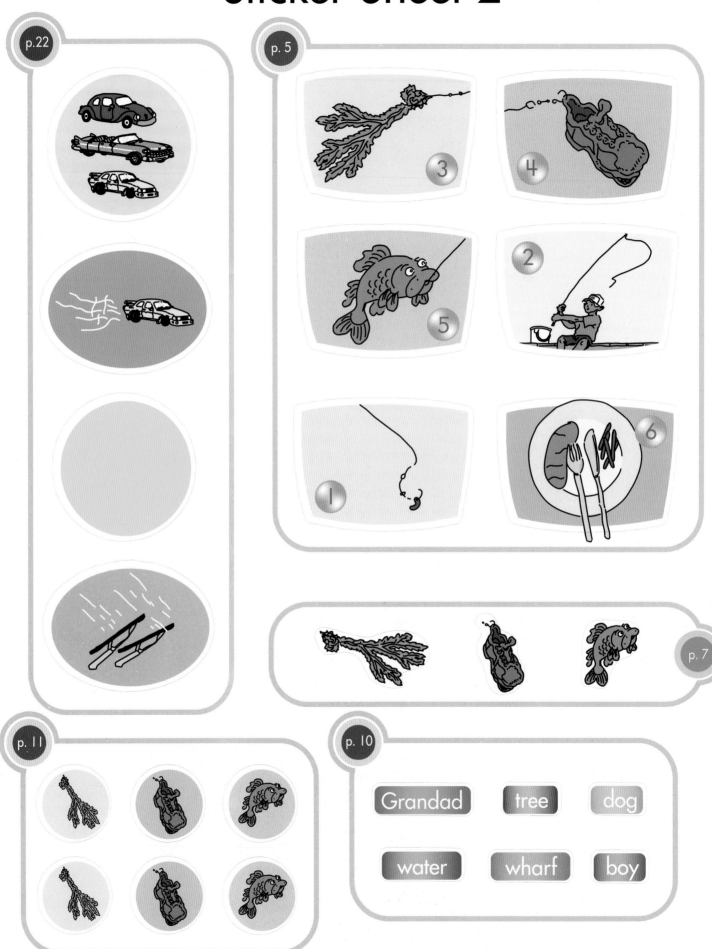

Sticker Sheet 3

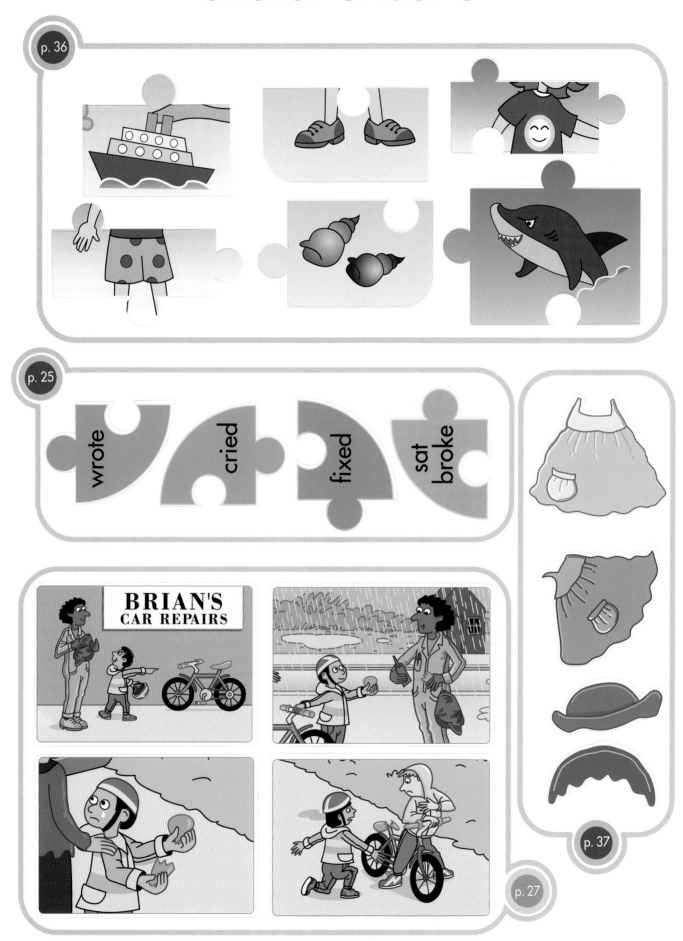

Sticker Sheet 4

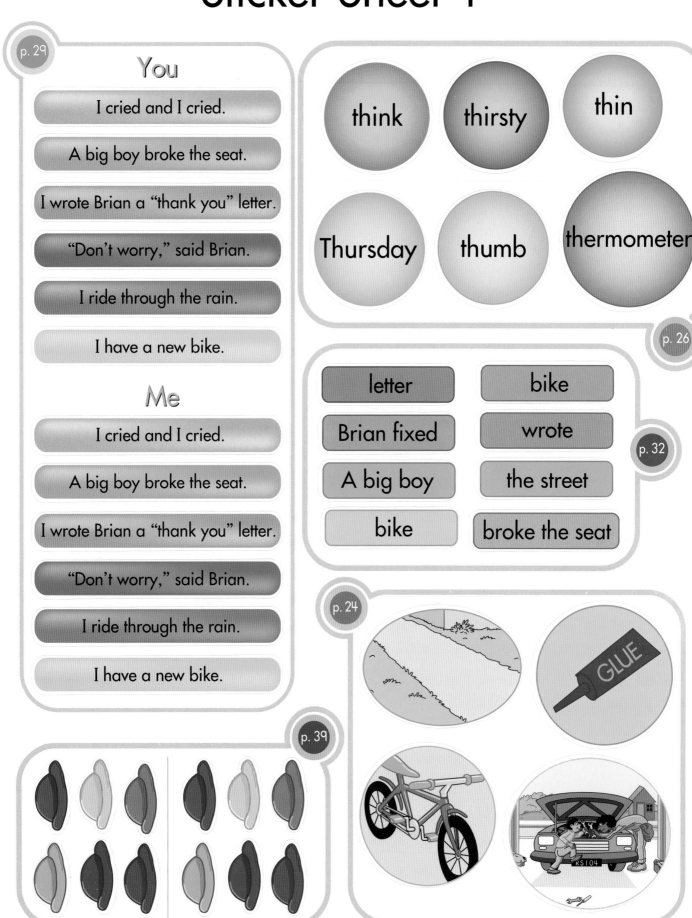

p. 29

You

I cried and I cried.

A big boy broke the seat.

I wrote Brian a "thank you" letter.

"Don't worry," said Brian.

I ride through the rain.

I have a new bike.

Me

I cried and I cried.

A big boy broke the seat.

I wrote Brian a "thank you" letter.

"Don't worry," said Brian.

I ride through the rain.

I have a new bike.

p. 26

think

thirsty

thin

Thursday

thumb

thermometer

p. 32

letter

bike

Brian fixed

wrote

A big boy

the street

bike

broke the seat

p. 24

GLUE

p. 39

Sticker Sheet 5

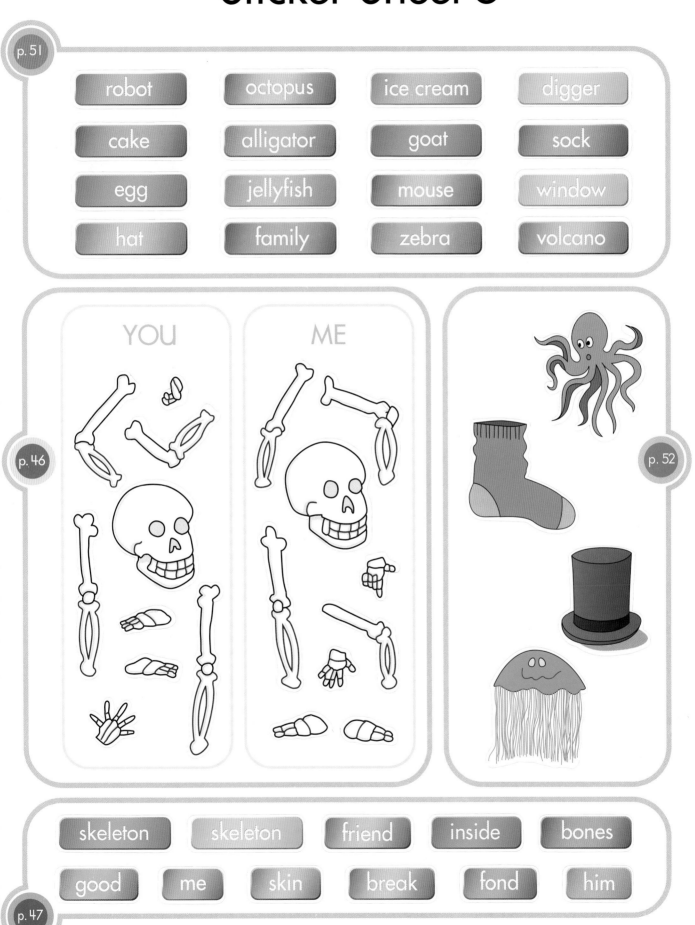

Sticker Sheet 6

Sticker Sheet 7

Sticker Sheet 8

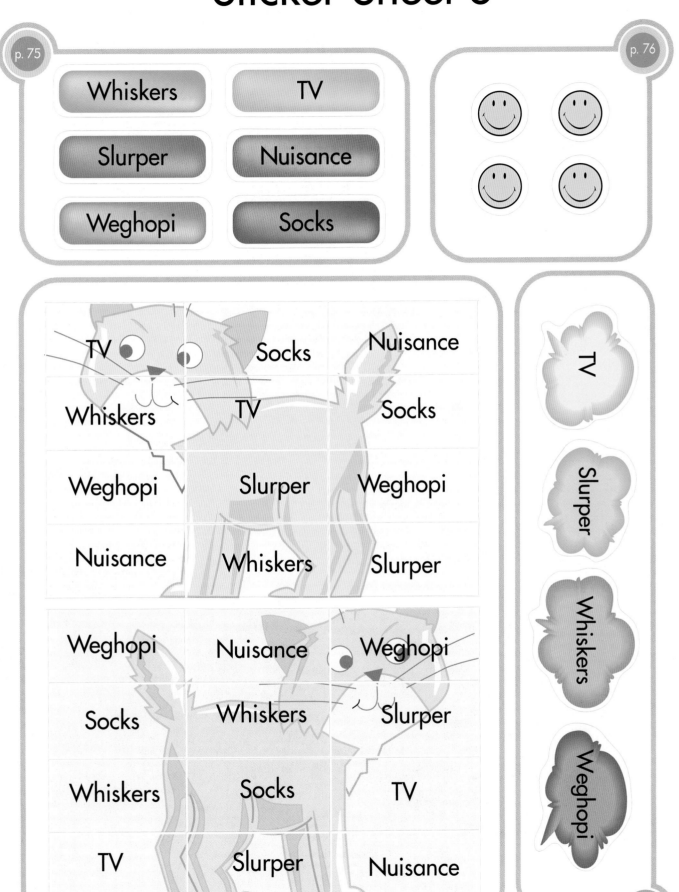

Sticker Sheet 9

p. 89

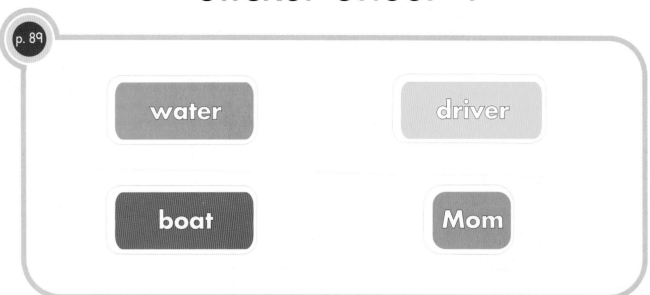

water

driver

boat

Mom

p. 87

Sticker Sheet 10

p. 98

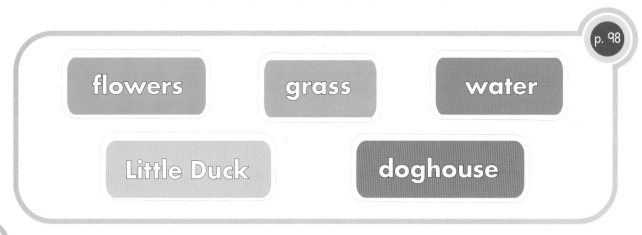

flowers

grass

water

Little Duck

doghouse

p. 102

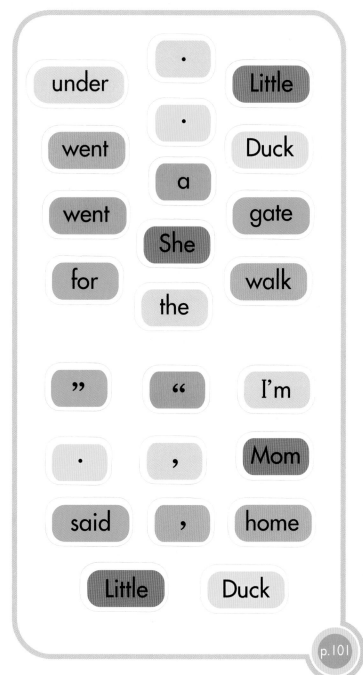

under

went

went

for

.

.

a

She

the

Little

Duck

gate

walk

"

.

said

"

,

,

I'm

Mom

home

Little

Duck

p. 101

Sticker Sheet 11

Sticker Sheet 14

p. 142

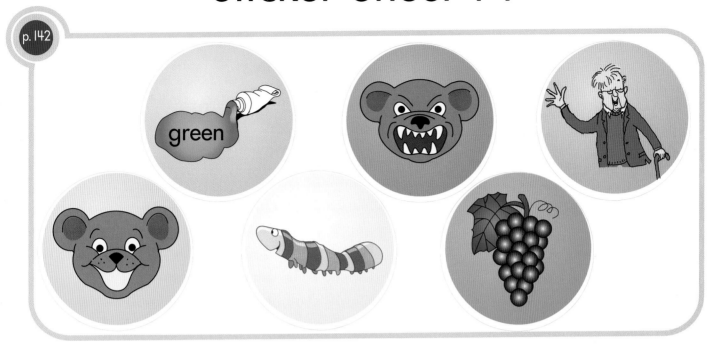

p. 136

p. 135

p. 141

Sticker Sheet 15

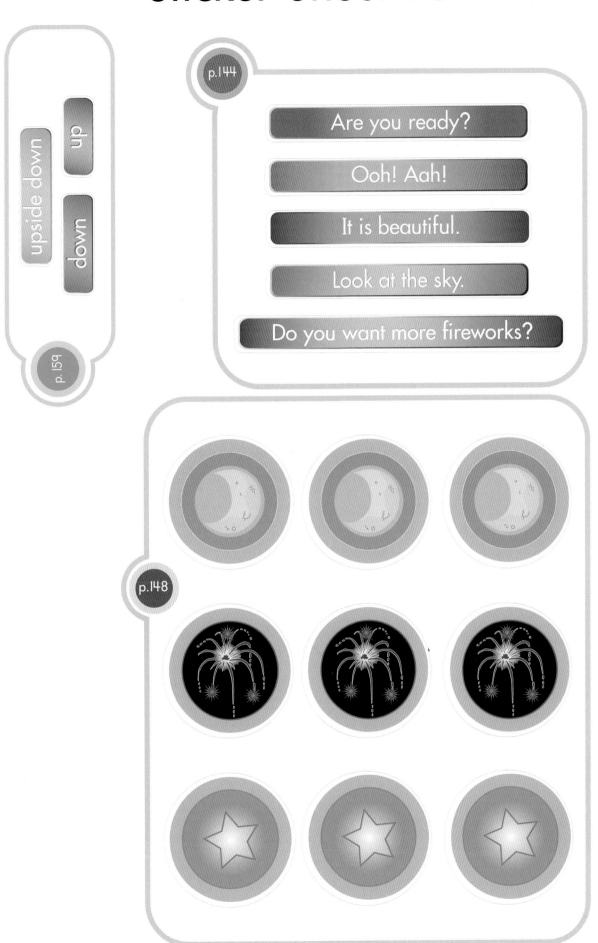

upside down

up

down

p.159

p.144

Are you ready?

Ooh! Aah!

It is beautiful.

Look at the sky.

Do you want more fireworks?

p.148